Teacher's ELL Handbook
Strategies for English Language Learners

Prentice Hall
Biology

by Nancy Montgomery, Ed.D.

PEARSON

Prentice Hall

Boston, Massachusetts
Upper Saddle River, New Jersey

Nancy Vincent Montgomery, Ed. D., has worked with English Language Learners for 30 years, beginning upon her graduation from Southern Illinois University in Carbondale, Illinois, with a Bachelor of Science degree in education. While teaching she was awarded two education grants to implement literacy projects with English Language Learners and was honored with a Teacher of the Year award. Her pursuit of two Master's degrees and a doctorate in education allowed her to continue her research in second language writing, literacy, and assessment. In addition, her many opportunities to visit other countries and study their cultures helped her to gain a true understanding of the complexities of learning a new language and a new culture. She has taught at an international school in Asia, and has completed field research in schools in Africa, Asia, Europe, and Latin America. She is currently a senior consultant for a Language and Literacy Cooperative in Dallas, Texas, where she resides.

ISBN 0-13-115333-1
7 8 9 10   10 09 08 07

Contents

To the Teacher

In the past decade there have been an increasing number of students entering U.S. public schools from multiple linguistic and cultural backgrounds. The number of Americans identifying themselves as Hispanic, for example, grew by nearly 60 percent since the 1990 census, roughly three million people more than predicted by the Census Bureau. The unexpected increase in the population of people from non-English-speaking cultures presents a major challenge for our schools: to create an optimal learning environment that will ensure comprehension for every student in all content areas of the curriculum.

This Handbook and Prentice Hall's *Biology* program can help you meet this challenge. As you know, English Language Learners face a number of language-related obstacles to learning that are compounded by the specialized nature of content-area subjects. For example, English Language Learners with little or no experience using English text will find it difficult to move from narrative to expository text, and to develop hypotheses and make inferences from a textbook. The more sophisticated sentence structure of high school materials and the need for more advanced study skills at this level contribute to the difficulty of understanding content material. Science, in particular, can prove difficult for the English Language Learner due to its technical vocabulary and the student's limited prior knowledge.

Teachers of ELL students face their own challenges. For instance, the language skills of ELL students can vary widely. Students who have been in our schools three years or fewer may still be acquiring Basic Interpersonal Communication Skills (BICS). Other students who have been in our schools five years or longer may have developed BICS but are still acquiring Cognitive Academic Language Proficiency Skills (CALPS). Even those students who have attained a high level of CALPS may need additional language support through second-language strategies.

Understanding the part that BICS and CALPS play in the comprehension of concepts will help the content-area teacher when teaching students with varying English language skills. The four language skills—reading, writing, speaking, and listening—need to be developed along with the specialized content-area material for ELL students to completely comprehend a subject. These students also need sheltered instruction to be successful, because they often have limited schooling experience and background knowledge of the content area, and lack technical and specialized vocabulary.

Using This Handbook

Since the key to teaching ELL students is in presenting comprehensible material, awareness of the oral language proficiency level of your students and the strategies that will effectively meet their needs is most important. The Oral Language Proficiency Chart on page 9 summarizes the characteristics of each level of language, instructional ideas for teachers, and performance indicators for students. The chart is followed by detailed explanations of each level of language. General strategies for the teacher and student, graphic organizers that are appropriate for English Language Learners, and vocabulary and comprehension strategies are also included in this Handbook. Transparencies of the graphic organizers are included for use as starting points. Also, alternative methods of assessment for ELL students at all levels of language proficiency are suggested.

The later pages of the Handbook show how the pedagogy and features of Prentice Hall *Biology* aid the success of the English Language Learner. These pages also contain sample lessons from Prentice Hall *Biology* that show how to apply the strategies in this Handbook to lesson content.

Language Proficiency Levels

Like all content areas, biology can prove difficult for English Language Learners. The specialized vocabulary and complexity of the subject matter, coupled with students' typically scant prior knowledge of science and limited English proficiency, can cause frustration for ELL students and for teachers who need to reach all students. Biology teachers, therefore, need to be familiar with the levels of oral language proficiency and with some instructional tools that will make scientific material comprehensible for the English Language Learner. This information is outlined in the chart on page 9 and explained in more detail below.

There are five levels of oral language proficiency. Levels I and II are considered beginning levels. Levels III and IV are intermediate levels, and Level V is the advanced, or transitional, level. Each level has distinct characteristics that have implications for instruction.

Characteristics of the English Language Learner: Beginning Level

- The beginning-level student has minimal to very limited comprehension of the English language. It is important to realize that this student is acquiring Basic Interpersonal Communication Skills (BICS), which can take up to three years.

- Student's speech will range from nothing to one or two individual words to phrases of two or three words.

- Many students at this level go through a silent period, in which they do not speak or even attempt to speak. This stage is common and can last from just a few hours to three months or perhaps longer. Keep in mind that these students are listening, observing, and learning language, even though it may appear that they are not. In fact, they may know some English but be too shy to speak. Verbalization depends on the individual student and his or her prior experiences with school. Do not force students to speak during this time. Allow them to speak their native language with one another or with you, if possible, for clarification of information.

What Beginning-Level Students Can Do: Performance Indicators

- Students can point to responses.

- They can label diagrams, illustrations, and maps. Many students who can neither speak nor comprehend English can illustrate a concept and label a map or diagram if they are given a sample. This activity gives students practice writing in English and helps them connect English words to a visual.

- They can use "yes" and "no" cards, gestures, manipulatives, or lab equipment to show understanding.

Instructional Ideas for Teachers of Beginning-Level Students

- Focus on vocabulary building through the use of visuals and concrete objects.
- Develop concepts through the use of graphic organizers, but keep them simple; beginning-level students can easily become confused and frustrated with graphic organizers that have many lines or circles.
- Play games that require nonverbal responses; for example, games in which students match words to pictures or diagrams. Students can also use "yes" and "no" cards to indicate understanding. Any activities that require nonverbal responses are called Total Physical Response activities.
- Give students an opportunity to build comprehension by developing open-ended sentences using words the students already know, words from a word bank, and words posted in the classroom.

Characteristics of the English Language Learner: Intermediate Level

- There is a noticeable increase in the student's comprehension.
- The student's sentence structure varies from simple to complex.
- The student is able to engage in conversation at a deeper level.
- The student's errors in speech vary from simple to complex. The student moves beyond the present tense and uses plurals with ease.
- Students at this level are attaining or have attained Cognitive Academic Language Proficiency Skills (CALPS).

What Intermediate-Level Students Can Do: Performance Indicators

- Students can use complete sentences ranging in structure from simple to complex.
- They participate in class discussions more easily and at a deeper level.
- They integrate higher-order thinking skills, such as debating, evaluating, and analyzing, into group discussions.

Instructional Ideas for Teachers of Intermediate-Level Students

- Use higher-level graphic organizers and visuals.
- Structure group discussions to encourage students to speak.
- Use Cloze activities (discussed on page 18) for vocabulary and concept building.
- Structure questions that require complete answers to encourage higher-order thinking skills.

Characteristics of the English Language Learner: Advanced Level

- The student is nearly proficient in English speech.
- The student has a higher level of comprehension.
- The student may lack writing experience in his or her native language as well as in English.
- The student's vocabulary may be near the level of a native speaker.
- Students at this level have attained a high level of Cognitive Academic Language Proficiency Skills (CALPS).

What Advanced-Level Students Can Do: Performance Indicators

- Students incorporate higher-order thinking skills in writing and speaking.
- Their participation in problem solving is near the level of participation of native speakers.
- They use more advanced vocabulary in debates, discussions, or other situations involving intensive communications.
- They show little hesitancy to speak.
- They do not require as many instructional modifications.
- They can complete all performance indicators listed on the Oral Language Proficiency Chart.

Instructional Ideas for Teachers of Advanced-Level Students

- Continue vocabulary building throughout lessons.
- Continue providing opportunities for students to use higher-order thinking skills.
- Integrate writing as well as reading into lessons, as many transitional students will be weak in writing skills.

Oral Language Proficiency Chart

Levels of Proficiency ELL CATEGORIES	Level I Pre-Production Stage	Level II Early Production Stage	Level III Speech Emergence	Level IV Intermediate Fluency Stage	Level V (Transitional) Near Proficient
	Beginning		Intermediate		Advanced
Characteristics of the English Language Learner	• Minimal comprehension • May be very shy • No verbal production • Non-English speaker • Silent period (10 hours to 3 months) • Uses gestures and actions to communicate	• Limited comprehension • Gives one- or two-word responses • May use two- or three-word phrases • Stage may last 6 months to 2 years	• Comprehension increases • Errors still occur in speech • Simple sentences • Stage may last 2 to 4 years	• Good comprehension • Sentences become more complex • Engages in conversation • Errors in speech are more complex	• Few errors in speech • Orally proficient • Near-native vocabulary • Lacks writing skill • Uses complex sentences
What They Can Do: Performance Indicators	• Listen • Point • Illustrate • Match • Choose	• Name • List and group • Categorize • Label • Demonstrate	• Compare and contrast • Recall and retell • Summarize • Explain	• Higher-order thinking skills • Analyze, debate, justify	• All performance indicators
Instructional Ideas for Teachers	• Visual cues • Tape passages • Pair students • Total Physical Response activities • Concrete objects • Graphic organizers	• Short homework assignments • Short-answer quizzes • Open-ended sentences	• Graphs • Tables • Group discussions • Student-created books • Cloze activities	• Group panels • Paraphrasing • Defending and debating	• Lessons on writing mechanics • Free reading of appropriate books • Cooperative learning groups

Strategies for Relating to English Language Learners

There are a number of basic strategies teachers can implement to meet the needs of their English Language Learners. In fact, these are common-sense, everyday strategies that teachers in all content areas already know and use. These strategies lay the foundation for a positive learning relationship between the student and the teacher.

Simplify Your Teacher Talk

One of the most important strategies is modifying and simplifying your "teacher talk," or the way you speak to your students during instruction. Often the vocabulary and sentence structure that teachers use are beyond the comprehension of their students. To avoid this problem, speak directly and succinctly, using simple words and sentences with students who are at a beginning-language level. Since ELL students are learning a new language as well as new academic concepts, avoid using slang or idiomatic expressions, which can add to their confusion. Using body language to emphasize important words or rephrasing a sentence or definition will also aid the English Language Learner in understanding new information.

Learn About Your Students' Heritage

You do not need to be able to speak a second language in order to make your ELL students feel you are interested in them. Learn as much as you can about the cultures and languages represented by the students in your classroom. Not only will you increase your own knowledge, but you will enhance the self-esteem of your students as they become aware of your interest in their heritage. You can also use your knowledge to broaden the horizons of the English-speaking students in your class.

Limited English Proficiency Does Not Mean Limited Thinking Skills

English Language Learners possess higher-order thinking skills, but many times it is believed that because the students are not proficient in English, they do not have those skills. Encourage hypothesizing, analyzing, inferring, asking questions, and making predictions, as well as other thinking skills. Students need opportunities to observe and use these skills in the classroom, as explained in the various strategy sections of this Handbook.

Give ELL Students Time to Respond

Increase response "wait time" for English Language Learners. These students must process information in two languages and will respond more quickly in a relaxed, risk-free environment. Then repeat the student's response in a natural manner in standard English. Repeating the response correctly will validate the student's response.

Give ELL Students a Sneak Preview

Provide an outline or list of instructions and review these with your ELL students. Give them an opportunity to look ahead in the text or view a model of the assignment. By doing so, you also inform students of your expectations.

Watch for Nonverbal Signals

English Language Learners use a number of nonverbal signals to show lack of understanding. These may include lowering the head, avoiding eye contact, covering the assignment paper, or simply a general look of confusion. Watch for these signs and be prepared to provide individual attention or assign the student to a partner in the classroom for help.

Provide a Risk-Free Learning Environment

Many English Language Learners come from cultures in which they were taught not to question the teacher, critique the information presented, or in general request clarification, simplification, or repetition. Some ELL students do not ask for help because their lack of English language proficiency makes them feel uncomfortable. Often these students will nod their head in agreement, smile, and appear to understand exactly what you are saying—until their test results prove otherwise.

Be prepared to teach students that it is acceptable to ask questions and critique information presented. At the same time try to provide a risk-free environment that will foster questioning, no matter what students' level of language proficiency. Help your students view you as being sensitive to their needs and as someone who will provide guidance in understanding content material.

Allow Students to Use Their Native Language

Let students know that it is acceptable to use their native language in the classroom. One way is to allow students to use their native language during student-to-student collaboration. Because many ELL students feel that their native language is not valued, you may want to use your knowledge of the students' language in instruction. This not only helps those students with very limited English proficiency, but also shows acceptance and appreciation of the students' native language.

Vocabulary Instruction for English Language Learners

Vocabulary can be particularly difficult for the English Language Learner, especially in biology and other sciences, because science vocabulary is usually technical and specialized. ELL students come from a variety of schooling backgrounds and may have limited experience with science. To complicate matters, many English words have more than one meaning, depending on the context in which they are used.

Take the word *table*, for example. In common English usage, the word *table* refers to a piece of furniture with legs and a flat horizontal surface. But in science, a table is a display of data in columns and rows. Often ELL students will translate an English word into their native language based on the most common usage of the word. For example, Spanish-speaking students may translate *table* as *mesa*, the piece of furniture. Or they may expect the English word to be similar to the word in their native language, in which case they may translate *table* as *tabla*, and then proceed to interpret it as *board* instead of *chart*. Because of these factors, teachers should use instructional strategies such as the ones below when introducing ELL students to new vocabulary.

Instructional Strategies

Relate New Words to Past and Present Experiences

Vocabulary instruction is most effective when it links new vocabulary to the background knowledge and experiences of the students as well as to words and concepts students are studying at the time. Associating new words with past and present learning experiences and showing the connection between the words and real life will improve students' comprehension. You can use direct questioning techniques to find out which words the students have already learned and how they learned them. If students lack background knowledge in a specific area, then you should build background before presenting content material.

Teaching a word out of context (that is, in isolation) can be effective, however, if the instruction involves motivating the student's interest in the word through visuals, demonstrating the use of the word, and showing a connection between the student and the word.

Make a Science Glossary

Allow students to make their own science glossaries as new words are introduced. This will give them practice reading and writing the word and will provide them with a reference. Briefly define each word. Invite students to draw a picture of the word, to include examples of synonyms, and to write the word in their native language if needed.

Provide Conversational Opportunities

Provide your English Language Learners with meaningful conversational opportunities in a risk-free environment. One strategy is to place students in cooperative groups, which gives them an opportunity to interact verbally with other students and to practice English sounds.

When designing cooperative grouping for the science classroom, do not place all English Language Learners in the same group. Their vocabulary skills will improve faster if they are integrated throughout the class with native English speakers. It is best, however, not to place beginning-level ELL students with the most advanced English speakers. Instead, place beginning ELL students with average achievers and intermediate or advanced ELL students with high achievers.

Use New Vocabulary in Writing and Homework Assignments

Design writing assignments so that students practice using the new words. Students need to develop a feel for how the vocabulary looks in writing, as well as how it sounds when spoken. Seeing the vocabulary written down helps students understand the structure and patterns of the English language. These assignments will help students develop good writing skills as well as foster vocabulary growth. For many English Language Learners, English may be their second spoken language, but their first written language.

Include the new vocabulary in take-home class assignments as well, so that vocabulary will be used outside of class. This reinforces the use of the new words and shows the relevance of the words to daily life. In addition, give students permission to incorporate illustrations of vocabulary words in writing assignments, class work, and homework. This is especially important for the beginning-level student.

Teach Independent Word-Analysis Strategies

Teach students word-analysis strategies so that new words can be attacked independently. For example, teach the prefix and/or suffix and the root of the designated vocabulary word. Write the meaning of the prefix and/or suffix and the root word on the board and have students do the same in their science glossaries. By providing this information whenever a new word is presented, students learn how to decode unfamiliar words and at the same time add new information to their glossaries for future reference. Teaching word-analysis skills also helps students understand how language works—knowledge that cannot be assumed, since English Language Learners come from all levels of schooling and background experiences.

Provide Independent Reading Opportunities

Have available in the classroom independent reading materials that relate to the content being studied and that use the new vocabulary words. These materials give students the opportunity to see the words used in context but in a leisure reading or research setting. Independent reading material might include trade and reference books as well as picture books that are interesting and age appropriate.

Increase Students' Exposure to New Words

Give students as much exposure as possible to new vocabulary words. The following paragraphs describe how.

- Post the words on a Word Wall in patterns that are easy for students to recognize. For example, words can be arranged in alphabetical order, in word families (such as by prefix or suffix), or organized by topic or concept. English Language Learners should understand how the words were chosen and how they relate to the content being studied. The Word Wall must also be an interactive instructional tool. Refer to the words often, use them in instruction, and assign them in homework to validate their study.

- Use the words in a graphic organizer. Many types of graphic organizers are appropriate for vocabulary study. The most important consideration is that the graphic organizer reflect the language level of the learner. A graphic organizer that is too complex will easily confuse the beginning-level English Language Learner. Likewise, a very simple graphic organizer will not be effective for ELL students who are at the advanced level.

- Incorporate new vocabulary words into daily instruction. Modeling the use of new words allows students to hear those words pronounced correctly and in the proper context. It teaches students how to determine meanings based on semantic and syntactic clues. It also validates the study of the words. If these words are used throughout the instruction, students realize they must be important.

- Display photographs, illustrations, or physical examples of the words being taught. English Language Learners can more accurately internalize the meaning of a word if they are able to see a visual representation of it. Allow students to draw their own pictures of what words mean. From their drawings you should be able to infer how much prior knowledge they have and how much background information must be presented before moving on to new material.

- Students must see the assigned words in the text they are using in the classroom. Go through the text and point out the vocabulary words being studied so that students are aware that the new words appear in the assigned texts.

In summary, vocabulary acquisition by English Language Learners is best accomplished when the students are given opportunities to see, hear, and illustrate the words, to categorize them, to connect them to what is being studied, and to connect them to real life.

Choosing the Words You Teach

You will need to provide English Language Learners with explicit prior instruction on a limited number of technical vocabulary words related to the topic they are going to study. The number of words you preteach depends on the language levels represented in the classroom. But how do you decide which words are most important for students to know? Use the following steps to help you choose.

1. First, assess students' prior knowledge of the topic using a graphic organizer or by direct questioning. Find out how much students already know about the topic before addressing specific vocabulary words.

2. Decide which vocabulary words are important for understanding the topic. Choose vocabulary words that can be represented visually, especially for the beginning- and intermediate-level students. The words should be crucial to understanding the text and are especially good choices if the words illustrate a common point such as the use of a prefix, suffix, or root word.

3. Check to see which words students will encounter again and again in the biology text. These words should be taught first. Make sure that key vocabulary is aligned with the expected learner outcomes.

4. Assess students' prior knowledge of the chosen vocabulary. Brainstorm by putting students into groups and listing the words they already know about the topic to be taught. This should give you some indication of the level of knowledge the students already have of the new vocabulary. (Remember to integrate beginning-level ELL students with native English speakers. Little brainstorming in English will take place in a group of all non-native speakers.)

5. Finally, ask yourself, What must I do as a teacher to make this vocabulary comprehensible to all of my students?

Sample Vocabulary Strategies

The following are several basic vocabulary strategies that can be used with both ELL students and English speakers.

List-Group-Label

List-Group-Label is a good vocabulary brainstorming activity for the English Language Learner. Students work in groups to list, group, and label words related to the topic being taught using the criteria in the box on the following page. Students will be more productive if they are grouped heterogeneously rather than by language levels. When students are grouped heterogeneously, they hear English spoken at different levels of proficiency, and they are more apt to participate than when they are grouped with students of the same language level.

When the groups have completed their lists, a student from each group reads the list and explains to the rest of the class why the words were grouped and labeled as they were. For a variation of this strategy, begin by providing students with one list of words and have students label and group them.

Criteria for List-Group-Label

List: Begin with the list of boldface vocabulary terms for the text lesson you are studying. Then, think of any other word or words that relate to the topic.

Group: Review the list of words and then group them in some way. Each group must contain at least three words, and words may appear in more than one group.

Label: For each group, think of a title that indicates the shared relationship between the words.

Building a Science Glossary

Building a science glossary helps English Language Learners see how language works. This strategy is designed for students to work independently, but pair grouping is beneficial for students who are non-English speakers.

Choose the words for this strategy, and have visuals available for each word. Model how to divide each word into parts (prefix, root word, suffix), determine the meaning of the word, pronounce the word with and without the prefix or suffix, and then use the word in a sentence. Post a list of common prefixes and suffixes in the room. This will enable your students to determine meanings on their own during independent work. The students can then add the words to their science glossary, placing the words in alphabetical order as they are added.

The English Language Learners will come to regard their own glossaries as more important than the classroom dictionary because the glossaries provide not only a pronunciation and definition, but a picture of what the word means as well. The glossary also reinforces the use of the English alphabet, which is important, as not all ELL students have a solid basis in the English alphabet.

How Do I Analyze a Word?

The following strategy gives students practice comparing and contrasting vocabulary words used in the text. Students list items that are similar to and different from the vocabulary word, and then tell in which way the item is similar to or different from the given word. Since these lists will often need research, this strategy gives students practice using reference materials. Model this strategy and then give groups or pairs the opportunity to complete it independently.

Word Analysis Chart

Word(s): lens (of eye)

Define or rename: (text definition or teacher-led definition)

Compare

lens of camera—focuses light
lens of microscope—focuses light

Contrast

pupil—lets in light
iris—adjusts size of pupil

What does it look like? (student illustration)

What Do I Know About the Word?

Place students into heterogeneous language-level groups of two or three at the most. Have each group draw a T-chart on a sheet of paper. (A T-chart consists of a horizontal line across the top of the page and a vertical line down the middle.) Have students label the left column "What I Know" and the right column "What I Have Learned."

Give students a word that they are going to study in the assigned selection. Have students list what they already know about the word in the left column. After studying the selection, have students revisit the chart and add what they have learned about the word to the right column. When they have finished, discuss with students what they have learned about the selected word. From the charts and the discussion, you should get a good idea of how well students understand the vocabulary word.

Topic: Fossils

What I Know	What I Have Learned
Very old	Index fossils
Found in rocks	Relative dating
May be bones	Radioactive dating

Comprehension Strategies for English Language Learners

The goal of every teacher is to make the material he or she is teaching comprehensible for all students. Teachers of English Language Learners can accomplish this goal by eliminating linguistic features of the text that will impede students' comprehension. In some cases, this means clarifying the text by adding language or rewriting sentences using simpler vocabulary. In other cases, it means supplementing the text with visual and audio aids while teaching ELL students specific reading strategies to improve comprehension. In all cases, adapting and modifying the text is key to developing students' oral and written comprehension skills. Following are some general guidelines for making the text more accessible for ELL students.

General Guidelines

1. Review the text and choose the important passages for your students to read.
   - Keep the length of the passages short—one to three paragraphs that emphasize the main points of the selection.
   - Use the Oral Language Proficiency Chart on page 9 to help you decide how much the students can comprehend at their language level.
2. Have visual support available. Visuals give context to the selection, aid in comprehension of the text, and remind the readers of what they have read.
3. Quickly locate and analyze words that will be difficult for your students. Preteach this vocabulary so the students will have fewer obstacles as they read the text.
4. During discussions, occasionally substitute simpler vocabulary for content-based vocabulary. For example, use *windpipe* and *trachea* interchangeably for the benefit of the ELL students.
5. Whatever visuals, modification techniques, and oral instruction you use should relate to the material in the text.

Specific Comprehension Strategies

The following are some specific strategies you can use to improve the reading comprehension of your ELL students.

Cloze Strategy

The Cloze strategy can be used for pre- and post-assessments as well as for comprehension checks during reading. This exercise will help you determine not only the extent of your students' vocabulary but how well they comprehend what they read. Below are some guidelines that can be used to develop a Cloze for the English Language Learner.

1. Choose a passage for your students to read that is at the appropriate language level.

2. Leave the first and last sentences intact, but delete important words from the sentences in between. The first and last sentences are left because they are usually introductory and concluding sentences, and they help the students determine the meaning of the missing words.

3. The difficulty of the deleted words must correspond to the language levels of the students in the classroom. Have students read or review the passage and use one of the following methods to replace the words that have been deleted:

   • Write in words from a teacher-provided word bank.

   • Draw pictures that represent the deleted words.

   • Choose from two words in parentheses; the correct answer could range from obvious (for the beginning ELL student) to subtle (for the advanced student).

Cloze Strategy Models

These models are appropriate for beginning- to intermediate-level English Language Learners. The vocabulary used is taken directly from the paragraph in the book, so the student is not expected to call up vocabulary that is not yet acquired.

Model I

Fill in the blanks with word-bank words.

The class Chondrichthyes contains sharks, rays, and skates. *Chondros* is the Greek word for cartilage, so the name of this class tells you that the skeletons of these fishes are built entirely of ___*cartilage*___. The cartilage of these animals is similar to the ___*flexible*___ tissue that supports your nose. Most cartilaginous fishes also have toothlike ___*scales*___ covering their skin. These scales make shark skin so rough that it can be used as sandpaper.

Word bank: flexible fishes scales cartilage shark

Model II

Fill in the blanks with one of the words in parentheses.

The kingdom Protista is composed of eukaryotic organisms that cannot be classified as animals, plants, or fungi. Of the six kingdoms, Protista is the _____least_____ (most, least) satisfying classification. That is because its members have the _____greatest_____ (least, greatest) variety. Most protists are _____single-celled_____ (single-celled, heterotrophic) organisms. Some protists are photosynthetic, while others are _____heterotrophic_____ (eukaryotic, heterotrophic). Some share characteristics with plants, others with fungi, and still others with animals.

QAR (Question-Answer Relationship) Strategy

In this strategy, English Language Learners learn about four types of questions, ranging from literal to analytical, and how to respond to each type. The strategy and vocabulary a student uses to answer a question will allow the teacher to determine the student's level of comprehension. The strategies are described below.

In the Book If the answer to the question can be found in the text, the student will use one of two In the Book strategies to formulate the answer.

1. **Right There:** The words used to formulate the question are taken directly from the text, so that the answer is "right there."

In the Book: Right There Model

Many traits are produced by the interaction of several genes. Traits controlled by two or more genes are said to be polygenic traits, which means "having many genes." For example, at least three genes are involved in making the reddish-brown pigment in the eyes of fruit flies.

Question: What are polygenic traits?

Answer Strategy: **In the Book: Right There**

Because the question was formed by restating a sentence from the text, students can find the answer to the question "right there," in the text. This is an example of a literal question and answer. This type of question would be appropriate for those students who are at the beginning or near intermediate level of English proficiency.

2. **Think and Search:** The answer can be found in the text, but it is spread over several sentences or paragraphs. The students must "think" about what the question is asking, then "search" the text for the answer.

In the Book: Think and Search Model

> Many traits are produced by the interaction of several genes. Traits controlled by two or more genes are said to be polygenic traits, which means "having many genes." For example, at least three genes are involved in making the reddish-brown pigment in the eyes of fruit flies.

Question: Why is the reddish-brown eye pigment in fruit flies a polygenic trait?

Answer Strategy: **In the Book: Think and Search**

The question combines two concepts in the text, and the answer to the question is distributed throughout the paragraph. Students must think about the question and then search the paragraph for the answer. This is another example of a literal question and answer; it is the Comprehension level of Bloom's taxonomy. This exercise is appropriate for intermediate-level students and for beginners who are paired with an English-speaking student.

In My Head If the question cannot be answered simply by reading the text but requires the student to use higher-order thinking skills, the student must use one of two In My Head strategies to formulate the answer.

1. **Author and You** The answer is not spelled out in the selection, although the text does provide clues. Students must use information from the text, combined with critical thinking skills, to draw conclusions, make inferences or predictions, or make generalizations in order to answer the question.

In My Head: Author and You Model

> Remember that the phenotype of an organism is only partly determined by its genotype. Many traits are strongly influenced by environmental, or nongenic, factors, including nutrition and exercise.

Question: How might exercise affect a person's phenotype?

Answer Strategy: **In My Head: Author and You**

The answer is not stated explicitly in the text. Students must use information from the text together with their own experiences to make the prediction.

Information: The environment influences an organism's phenotype.

Experience: Exercise can make people stronger.

Answer: Exercise can strengthen a person's bones and muscles.

This is an example of an analytical question; it combines the Analysis and Synthesis levels of Bloom's taxonomy. This exercise is appropriate for intermediate and advanced students, although you will need to model orally and visually how to arrive at the answer. Beginners should be exposed to this strategy but will not have the English language skills to complete this exercise (even though they possess the necessary higher-order thinking skills and could complete the exercise in their native language).

2. **On My Own** As in the Author and You strategy, the answer is not spelled out in the selection. Students use their own past experiences and prior knowledge to answer the question. However, unlike the Author and You strategy, the student's answers do not depend on the position of the author; that is, the answers are opinions. Using the On My Own strategy, there is no right or wrong answer.

In My Head: On My Own Model

> It would be marvelous to be able to cure hemophilia or other genetic diseases. But if human cells are to be manipulated to cure disease, should biologists try to engineer taller people or change their eye color, hair texture, sex, or appearance?

Question: What are appropriate uses of genetic engineering in humans?

Answer Strategy: **In My Head: On My Own**

Because the answer is an opinion, some students can answer this question without even reading the text. This is an example of an analytical question; it is at the application level of Bloom's taxonomy. This exercise is appropriate for high-intermediate and advanced levels, but students at all levels can benefit from this type of questioning. Beginning-level students should be exposed to this type of questioning, but the teacher needs to realize that the students' limited vocabulary and writing expertise will prevent them from writing or explaining their answer. Remember that while all

English Language Learners have the ability to do higher-order thinking, they may not be able to articulate their thoughts because of their limited language skills. Try having these students answer orally, with the help of an English-proficient partner. Answering On My Own questions can be very enriching for English Language Learners because it allows them to use higher-order thinking skills while developing their English vocabulary.

KWL Chart

A KWL chart (shown below and in Transparency 8) is a three-part chart that asks students to state what they already *know* about a topic, what they *want* to find out, and then what they have *learned* after reading about the topic. In short, the chart provides the student with a visual self-assessment of their knowledge about a particular topic before and after instruction. Just as important, the chart tells the teacher how much background knowledge students have about the topic, what students think is important to know about the topic, and students' level of comprehension after reading. The teacher will use this information to tailor his or her lessons accordingly and to reteach, if necessary.

This strategy will be most effective for ELL students if you complete the chart as a class and record their responses on a class KWL chart at the front of the room. That way students can share information, hear language spoken, and see the connection between the pronunciation of words and their written symbols.

Use Transparency 8 for your KWL chart. Have students draw the same chart on a sheet of paper. They may want to place the chart on their papers sideways, and place each head at the top of the columns formed.

What Do I KNOW?
What Do I WANT to Know?
What Have I LEARNED?

Brainstorm What You Already Know Ask students to brainstorm what they already know about the given subject. Encourage all students to participate. If necessary, pair English Language Learners with English speakers to accommodate students at all language levels. For example, allow beginning-level ELL students to answer in their native language and, with the help of another student, to translate their answer into English. Usually, they will answer with words or phrases, rather than in complete sentences.

Write all the information from the brainstorming session in the top box of the class KWL chart. Have students help you categorize the information. Then have students record their individual responses in the top box of their KWL chart.

Think About What You Want to Know Before they begin reading, ask students what they want to find out in the selection. Encourage them to respond in the form of a question (for example, What are the phases of the moon?). Record their questions in the middle box of the class chart. Then have students write the questions that are important to them in the middle box of their own KWL charts.

Review What You Have Learned After reading, have students fill in the "What have I LEARNED?" box of their KWL chart. Use the questions from the "What do I WANT to know?" section to guide the discussion.

Think-Pair-Share Strategy

English Language Learners learn discussion techniques in this follow-up comprehension activity. Keep in mind that the English language proficiency level of the students will impact the depth of discussion. In addition, the selection students read may have to be modified to allow for their language level and writing expertise. It is best to pair students for this exercise. To get the most benefit from this strategy, have the Word Wall in place for students' reference and allow them to use their student-developed science glossaries.

1. Have students read a selection you have chosen from the text, such as "Form and Function in Fishes," Chapter 30.

2. Suggest a topic from the selection, for example, "Feeding."

3. Have students work in pairs and write down what they have learned about the topic. Allow them to reread the selection for clarification if necessary.

4. Ask each pair of students to share their responses with the class. Record students' responses on an overhead, on chart paper, or on the chalkboard.

5. Conclude the activity with a class discussion in which students evaluate the responses, highlighting important points and eliminating inappropriate responses. Refer to the illustrations in the book to lend additional support to the evaluation process.

Graphic Organizers

A graphic organizer is a visual representation of knowledge organized into patterns. Graphic organizers are valuable teaching tools because they get students actively involved in learning and help them develop their critical and creative thinking skills. Constructing a graphic organizer requires the student to acknowledge, evaluate, understand, and restate information in a meaningful, systematic way. You might say that a graphic organizer is really a visual representation of the way our brains process and store information.

Graphic organizers are appropriate for all students in all content areas, but they are especially helpful to the English Language Learner. They help the ELL student focus on what is important, and by highlighting key vocabulary and concepts, they help the student remember them. Graphic organizers can also be used as alternative assessment tools. If each student constructs a graphic organizer before instruction, you can see what the student already knows about a topic. After instruction, a graphic organizer can tell you how well the student understands what he or she has been taught.

The rewards of using graphic organizers include the following:

- Students, in general, have a better attitude toward learning.
- Students have a better understanding and better retention of the material.
- If students collaborate on constructing graphic organizers, their socialization skills improve. They learn to negotiate, evaluate, and work together, even though some members of the group may not be English proficient.
- Students' questioning ability improves as they look for meaning in the material presented.
- Students come to understand that there are different ways of representing knowledge and that how we organize information is influenced by culture, language, personality, and prior knowledge.

How to Use Graphic Organizers

Graphic organizers are more effective for the English Language Learner if they are taught using the following instructional approach:

1. Explain the purpose of graphic organizers.
2. Choose a graphic organizer that is appropriate for the language level of your students and the nature of the information to be organized. You may have to modify the graphic organizer to meet the language needs of your students.
3. Demonstrate how to organize information in the graphic organizer before providing guided or independent practice.

4. Give students an opportunity to demonstrate understanding by designing their own graphic organizer based on the material studied. You can have students work in groups, in pairs, or individually, depending on their language level.

5. Post the student-designed graphic organizers. Students can refer to them as they work on future assignments.

6. To enhance the English Language Learner's understanding of a graphic organizer, you may want to do one or more of the following:

   - Provide illustrations of the information in the graphic organizer, followed by descriptive words about the illustrations.

   - Use color-coding for main concepts or for the steps in a process.

   - For variety, draw graphic organizers on the chalkboard, on an overhead, on chart paper, or on a mural.

Types of Graphic Organizers

There are two basic types of graphic organizers; the type you use with your English Language Learners will depend on the topic you are studying. Sequential graphic organizers, such as flowcharts and cycle diagrams, show a sequence of events or the steps or stages of a process. Conceptual graphic organizers, such as concept circles and maps, cause/ effect charts, compare/contrast charts, and Venn diagrams, show how concepts are related. The following section explains how to use these different types of graphic organizers with English Language Learners.

Flowchart (Transparency 1)

A flowchart is used to show a sequence of events in chronological order or the steps or stages in a process. Determine the number of boxes needed for the flowchart based on the information being presented. For example, one concept may call for only three boxes, whereas another concept may call for six. Just make sure the length and complexity of the flowchart are aligned with the English proficiency levels of your students. When simple illustrations can clarify the process, have students include them in the appropriate boxes. You may also want to color-code the steps. The following example shows the sequence of events in respiration.

The Path of Air

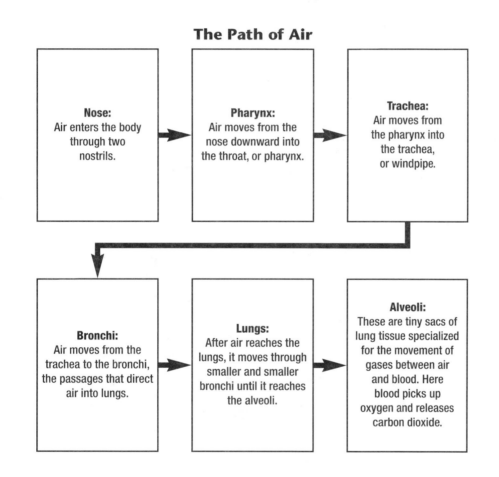

Cycle Diagram (Transparency 2)

A cycle diagram is similar to a flowchart in that it is used to show a sequence of events. In a cycle diagram, however, the sequence of events is continuous. Give students the opportunity to illustrate or build models of the steps to increase their comprehension of the cycle. The example of a cycle diagram below shows the life cycle of *Plasmodium*, the protist that causes malaria.

Life Cycle of
Plasmodium

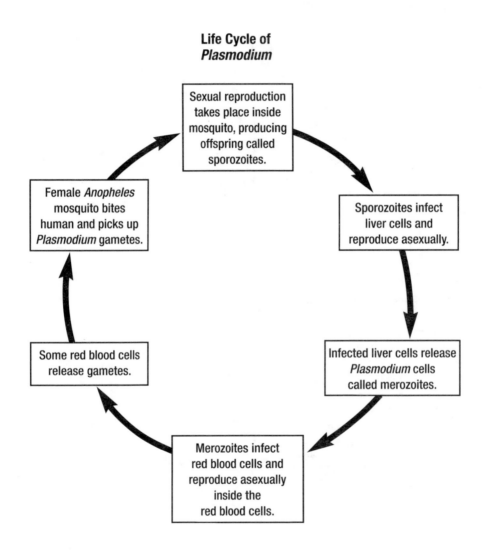

Concept Circle (Transparency 3)

A concept circle is a conceptual graphic organizer, which means it shows the relationship between a main concept or idea and supporting details. The main concept is written in a center circle, with the supporting details in boxes or circles around it. The supporting details are connected to the center circle with straight lines. To improve students' comprehension, have available illustrations of the supporting facts. In the concept circle below, for example, you might post an illustration of animals migrating when that particular subject is being taught.

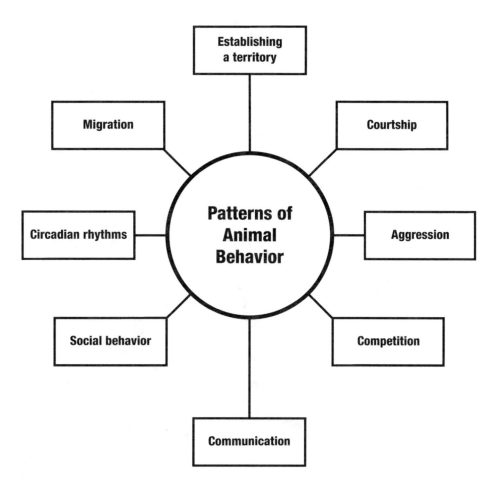

Modified Concept Map (Transparency 4)

A modified concept map or a hierarchical map is similar to a concept circle, but it is more detailed. The main concept is listed at the top, with successive levels of information underneath, each subordinate to the one above. Because of the hierarchical nature of concept maps, they can be quite complicated. You will need to decide how many subcategories to include in your organizer based on the language levels represented in your class. In general, to make the concept map more comprehensible for the English Language Learner, keep it simple; that is, place only the most important information on the map. You may also want to have illustrations or concrete objects available for students to examine.

The following concept map shows the main groups of plants, with their characteristics and examples.

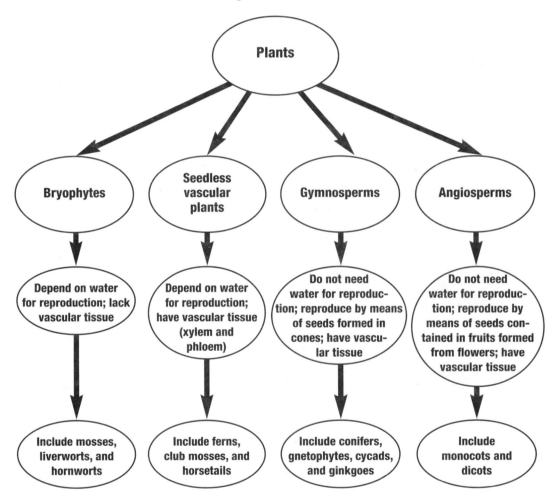

Cause/Effect Chart (Transparency 5)

A cause/effect chart is another way to show the relationship between concepts or facts. It will be more effective for the English Language Learner if it contains illustrations of the concepts presented.

Infectious Diseases

Cause (Pathogen)	Effect (Disease)
Virus	Common cold
Virus	Influenza
Bacteria (*Borrelia burgdorferi*)	Lyme disease
Bacteria (*Streptococcus pyogenes*)	Strep throat
Fungus	Athlete's foot
Protist	Malaria

Compare/Contrast Chart (Transparency 6)

A compare/contrast chart is another type of conceptual graphic organizer. It is used for categorizing the similarities and differences between two items. To improve this graphic organizer's effectiveness, provide illustrations and icons, and color-code important information.

Sexual Reproduction vs. Asexual Reproduction

Similarities	Differences
Results in new organisms	Sexual reproduction—two parents; asexual reproduction—one parent
Offspring receive genetic material from parent or parents	Sexual reproduction—offspring have mixture of genetic material from both parents; asexual reproduction—offspring are genetically identical to parent
Necessary for survival of species	Sexual reproduction—introduces genetic diversity to a population; asexual reproduction—no genetic diversity, but population can grow rapidly.

Venn Diagram (Transparency 7)

A Venn diagram is a conceptual graphic organizer that is used to show the similarities and differences between two or more sets of items. The Venn diagram consists of two (or more) overlapping circles with an area of commonality in the middle. To enhance your ELL students' comprehension, use illustrations along with words, and color or shade the overlap section of the diagram to emphasize elements the items have in common. You might also list the common elements below the diagram.

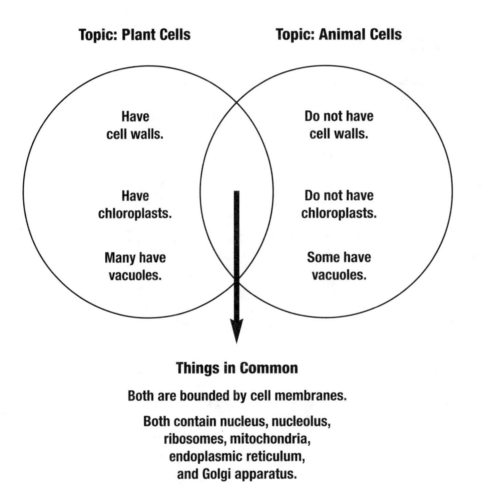

Topic: Plant Cells   **Topic: Animal Cells**

Have
cell walls.

Have
chloroplasts.

Many have
vacuoles.

Do not have
cell walls.

Do not have
chloroplasts.

Some have
vacuoles.

Things in Common

Both are bounded by cell membranes.

Both contain nucleus, nucleolus,
ribosomes, mitochondria,
endoplasmic reticulum,
and Golgi apparatus.

Authentic/Alternative Assessment Strategies

Teachers in all content areas have struggled to find assessment strategies that will accurately measure the knowledge and abilities of their English Language Learners. Research has shown that without appropriate assessment strategies, ELL students may be graded inappropriately and placed in classes or programs in which they are destined to fail. Finding appropriate assessment practices is difficult because of wide variations in the language proficiency levels and prior school experiences of ELL students as well as in the ELL expertise of their content area teachers. Standardized tests alone do not give an accurate picture of the academic performance of these students. Therefore, teachers with English Language Learners in their classroom should consider authentic/alternative assessment strategies that contain the following components.

Open-Ended Questions

Having students write answers to open-ended questions not only gives them a chance to demonstrate their writing skills, but it assesses how well students understand what they have read, fosters higher-order thinking skills, and also reveals any misconceptions students may have about the content material.

Student-Created Products and Reports

Working individually, in pairs, or in groups, students produce a product or deliver a written or oral report to show comprehension of the assignment. Examples of student-created products include projects, experiments, and demonstrations. Reporting methods might include a written paper or an oral explanation accompanied by charts or other visuals, depending on the language proficiency of the student.

When using this method of assessment, assign tasks that are challenging, keeping in mind students' level of language proficiency. The tasks should be authentic—that is, activities found in the real world that are relevant to students' lives. It is also important that you model the reporting method by showing examples of what is required of students and explaining how the products will be assessed. The advantage of this form of assessment is that you can evaluate a student's level of comprehension at each step of the assignment.

Student Self-Evaluation

Let the students tell you what they already know and what they want to learn about the topic. Then let them tell you what they learned, how they learned it, and how they will use what they have learned. This can be accomplished by keeping a science journal, filling out a self-evaluation chart on a particular lesson, or designing a graphic organizer such as a KWL chart (discussed on page 23).

Student Assessment Scales

Student assessment scales are an effective way for students to assess not only what they have learned but also what role they have played in completing a group assignment. This can be accomplished through simple questions on a student self-assessment page, for example: What did I contribute to the group in completing the assignment? How was I successful in completing the assignment? and What was one area of success?

For certain questions, you could have students assess themselves on a scale of 1–5 or 1–10. However, be aware of those students who assign themselves the very lowest number. Meet with them to discuss how they can improve their scores.

A variation of this is for the student to rate himself or herself while you rate the student. In most cases your scores will be similar. Consider it a "red flag"—especially for your English Language Learners—if the two scores vary widely.

Scientific Inquiry and English Language Learners

Scientific inquiry involves studying the natural world through objective analysis. It includes processes such as making observations, posing questions, identifying problems, formulating hypotheses, testing hypotheses through controlled experiments, collecting and interpreting data, and drawing conclusions on the basis of data. English Language Learners may have difficulty with methods of scientific inquiry partly because of their limited science background but also because of their lack of oral English proficiency, undeveloped English composition skills, and inexperience using higher-level thinking skills, such as analyzing and inferring, in English. The strategies suggested below will enable you to help your ELL students use scientific processes.

Posing Questions and Identifying Problems

In order to pose scientific questions or identify problems, students will need some background knowledge of the topic. Begin by brainstorming with students to determine how much they know about the topic. Use a graphic organizer such as a KWL chart or a modified concept map for the benefit of your English Language Learners. (These organizers are explained in detail on pages 23 and 30.)

It's possible that your ELL students will not have adequate background knowledge to identify a problem. Give all students a chance to build or reinforce background knowledge by researching the topic. Be sure to provide research materials, such as magazines and trade and reference books.

Following the brainstorming and research sessions, lead students to identify a problem by asking them a series of questions about it. Make sure that your questions can be understood by students at all levels of English proficiency. (See the Oral Language Proficiency Chart on page 9.) Be prepared to use visual prompts, such as pictures, charts, and even gestures, to make yourself understood.

Developing a Hypothesis

Once students have identified a problem, guide them to make a logical hypothesis based on their previous science experience and background knowledge of the topic. A hypothesis is a possible explanation for a set of observations. To help students understand this, model some sample problems and hypotheses on chart paper or on the board. For example:

Question: Why does the puppy bark all night?

Hypothesis: It barks because it is hungry.

You may want to place students in cooperative groups when developing their own hypotheses.

Designing and Conducting an Experiment

Guide students through the process of making a written plan for their experiment. Again, you may want to have ELL students work in pairs or cooperative groups with English speakers. Give each pair or group a sheet of drawing paper and have students record the steps of their experiment in both pictures and words. The design must include the following:

- A statement of the problem

- The steps of the experiment

- Illustrations or sketches of what the experimental setup will look like

- Student responsibilities while conducting the experiment

- A prediction of the results of the experiment

Collecting and Recording Data

Have students work in pairs or groups to collect and record data. Keep in mind, however, that English Language Learners at the same proficiency level should never be paired for data collection. Instead, pair students who have writing expertise with students who use illustrations or symbols to express themselves. Data collection should then take place as follows: One student takes accurate notes on the observations while the other student adds illustrations or diagrams or arranges the data. You may need to explain to your ELL students how to organize the data they collect—for example, by using data tables, sketches, or written observations. The best way to do this is to model the data collection process.

Interpreting the Data

For the benefit of your English Language Learners, copy students' data on sheets of chart paper and post them on the wall. Then, using different-color markers to represent different categories of information, have students circle information they feel is important to the experiment. Discuss with students what type of visual representation would work best for the data, and if it is a graph, discuss which data sets will be the variables. Once students have completed their graphs, have them look for trends in the data, paying particular attention to data that do not fit the trend. Discuss whether the anomalous data should be discarded or should be used to adjust the trend.

Drawing Conclusions

Begin by having students review the problem they identified or the question they posed. Next, have students make inferences about the problem based on the data they collected. Students must work cooperatively to come to a conclusion about the problem. Then have them compare their conclusion to their original hypothesis. Finally, discuss with students how their knowledge of or opinions about the topic have changed due to the results of the experiment.

Prentice Hall *Biology* and ELLs

Biology is friendly to the English Language Learner because it addresses the affective, linguistic, and cognitive aspects of learning. The chart below summarizes how the pedagogy and features of each chapter help English Language Learners understand new concepts presented in a language that is unfamiliar to them. *Biology* gives all students, regardless of language levels, the opportunity to use their imagination, to use skills such as observing, summarizing, and inferring, and to see that everyone can learn science and pursue a scientific career regardless of gender or ethnic background.

Inquiry Activity
- Activities relevant to real life motivate students to learn both the content and the language.
- Think About It questions give opportunities for critical thinking.

Guide for Reading
- Questions elicit important points so students can look for them in the reading. Boldface sentences summarize these points.
- Reading Strategies suggest activities to make the reading more meaningful.

Section Titles, Subsection Heads
- Titles help students understand what they will be reading.
- Section titles and subsection heads outline the content presented.

Vocabulary Words
- New science terms are listed on the first page of each section. Vocabulary is emphasized through the use of boldface type.
- Each term is defined in easy-to-read terms, and often is connected to a visual.
- The text allows students to infer the meaning of the vocabulary words through context clues.

Photographs, Diagrams, Charts, and Graphs
- Photos of real people representing diverse ethnic groups allow students to see themselves interacting with science concepts.
- Diagrams, charts, and graphs organize information for visual interpretation.
- Visuals and text are closely linked, giving students with less language proficiency a visual overview of concepts.

Checkpoint
- Ongoing comprehension checks let students know whether they understand key concepts.

Section Assessments
- Ongoing assessment helps students know whether they have grasped the basic content and can use their higher-level critical thinking skills.

Writing in Science
- Writing about science concepts provides language stimulation and opportunities to translate concepts into the students' own words.

Labs
- Clear, step-by-step instructions allow students to follow modeled procedures and to work in small, incremental steps.
- Labs allow students to reinforce new vocabulary and concepts by using manipulatives and laboratory equipment.

Sample Chapter:
Cell Growth and Division

Starting the Chapter: Inquiry Activity

If ELL students do not know how to use a microscope, model the procedure by setting up a microscope and slide and demonstrating how to focus the slide under low and high power.

Students need to understand that they will compare the sizes of cells in large plants to those in small plants, and the sizes of cells in large animals to those in small animals; they will not be comparing plant cells to animal cells. To help clarify this, show a photograph or illustration of a large plant, such as a tree, and a small plant, such as a blade of grass. Alongside each plant, show a photomicrograph of cells from that plant or a similar plant. The two cell photographs should be approximately the same magnification.

When they do the activity, beginning ELL students should be paired with students who are more proficient in English. Encourage students to express their answers to the Think About It questions by drawing pictures as well as writing words.

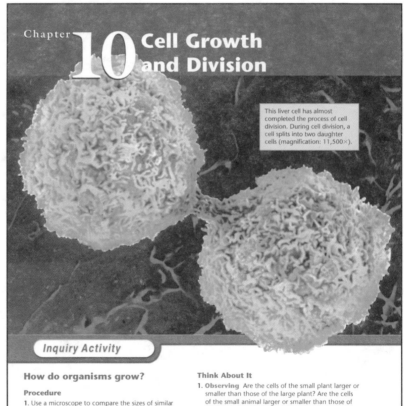

Chapter **10** Cell Growth and Division

This liver cell has almost completed the process of cell division. During cell division, a cell splits into two daughter cells (magnification: 11,500×).

Inquiry Activity

How do organisms grow?

Procedure

1. Use a microscope to compare the sizes of similar cells in large and small plants. For example, you might compare the leaf cells of grass to the leaf cells of a tree. Be sure to use the same magnification when comparing the sizes of the cells.

2. Use a microscope to compare the sizes of cells in similar tissues from small and large animals, such as muscle tissue from a frog and from a human.

Think About It

1. **Observing** Are the cells of the small plant larger or smaller than those of the large plant? Are the cells of the small animal larger or smaller than those of the large animal?

2. **Comparing and Contrasting** Make a general statement that compares the number and size of cells in small organisms to those in larger organisms.

240 *Chapter 10*

Section 10–1
Cell Growth

Preparing the Lesson

Assess Prior Knowledge

Review the structure of cells by calling attention to the illustrations of plant and animal cells in Chapter 7 (Figure 7–6, page 175). Ask students what they remember about cells from Chapter 7. List their responses on the board, correcting any misconceptions.

Say the word *nucleus* aloud, and write it on the board. Call on an ELL student to point to the nucleus in each illustration on page 175. Then review the term *chromosome,* making certain that students know that chromosomes are made of DNA and are located in the nucleus.

Vocabulary

Begin a Word Wall (discussed on page 14 of this Handbook) for the chapter. In addition to the Vocabulary term *cell division,* include *nucleus, chromosome, DNA,* and *cell membrane* as a review. For each word, write the definition and include a visual that represents the word. Use the Word Wall to preteach the term *cell division* and to review the other terms.

Point out that the term *cell division* consists of two words: *cell* and *division.* To demonstrate division, cut one or more objects, such as a sheet of paper and an orange, into halves. Ask students what must happen during cell division. Have students add *cell division* to their Science Glossaries (discussed on page 16 of this Handbook).

Reading Strategy

Model how to rewrite the heads as questions. Then pair ELL students to brainstorm answers to the questions.

Reading the Lesson

Limits to Cell Growth

Before Reading To help students understand the concept of limits, use familiar, everyday examples such as speed limit or limited time. Then, read the boldface sentence aloud. Clarify the phrase "the more demands the cell places" by asking volunteers to identify situations that put demands on people, for example, jobs put demands on workers.

10–1 Cell Growth

When a living thing grows, what happens to its cells? Does an animal get larger because each cell increases in size or because it produces more of them? In most cases, living things grow by producing more cells. On average, the cells of an adult animal are no larger than those of a young animal—there are just more of them.

Limits to Cell Growth

There are two main reasons why cells divide rather than continuing to grow indefinitely. **The larger a cell becomes, the more demands the cell places on its DNA. In addition, the cell has more trouble moving enough nutrients and wastes across the cell membrane.**

DNA "Overload" As you may recall, the information that controls a cell's function is stored in a molecule known as DNA. In eukaryotic cells, DNA is found in the nucleus of the cell. When a cell is small, the information stored in that DNA is able to meet all of the cell's needs. But as a cell increases in size, it usually does not make extra copies of DNA. If a cell were to grow without limit, an "information crisis" would occur.

To help understand why a larger cell has a more difficult time functioning efficiently than a smaller cell, compare the cell to a growing town. Suppose a small town has a library with a few thousand books. If more people move into the town, the town will get larger. There will be more people borrowing books, and sometimes people may have to wait to borrow popular titles. Similarly, a larger cell would have to make greater demands on its available genetic "library." In time, the cell's DNA would no longer be able to serve the increasing needs of the growing cell.

Exchanging Materials There is another reason why the size of cells is limited. You may recall that food, oxygen, and water enter a cell through its cell membrane. Waste products leave in the same way. The rate at which this exchange takes place depends on the surface area of the cell, which is the total area of its cell membrane. However, the rate at which food and oxygen are used up and waste products are produced depends on the cell's volume. Understanding the relationship between a cell's volume and its surface area is the key to understanding why cells must divide as they grow.

Guide for Reading

Key Concept
• What problems does growth cause for cells?

Vocabulary
cell division

Reading Strategy: Asking Questions Before reading this section, rewrite each blue heading as a *what, where,* or *how* question. Then, as you read, fill in the answer to each question.

▼ **Figure 10–1** Living things grow by producing more cells. Although the adult snail is larger than the young snail, the cells of both are the same size.

Cell Growth and Division **241**

Before Reading (continued) Preview the four subheads (DNA "Overload" and so forth) with students, to give them a sense of the structure of the lesson. To help students focus their reading, explain that they will construct a concept circle (discussed on page 29 of this Handbook) as they read. To model the process, draw a partially completed concept circle on the board. The center circle should contain the boldface sentences ("The larger a cell becomes, the more demands the cell places on its DNA. In addition, . . ."). Draw four large subcircles with lines connecting them to the center circle. In each subcircle, write one of the four text subheads (DNA "Overload," and so forth), leaving enough space for writing additional phrases. Tell students that they will write the most important ideas on each subtopic in their concept circles.

During Reading Have students begin by reading the text following DNA "Overload." To help clarify the ideas, use the analogy of a town library described in the second paragraph. Ask volunteers to explain, in their own words, what happens when a town keeps growing but the local library doesn't. Explore similar analogies with students—for example, a doctor's office with too many patients, a supermarket with many customers but not enough cashiers. Then model the process of filling in the concept circle by adding important words and phrases to the subcircle on the board for DNA "Overload."

Pair students and have them read the other three subsections. Members of each pair should collaborate to complete the concept circle.

The topic of surface area/volume ratios is difficult for many students to grasp. Point out Figure 10–2 and tell students to look at it carefully as they read Ratio of Surface Area to Volume. Also, supply students with metric rulers and blank paper so they can sketch cubes of different dimensions.

After Reading Call on volunteers to share their completed concept circles. Write their ideas in the circles on the board, correcting any errors and supplying any omissions.

To demonstrate the concept of surface/volume ratio, you might bring in a set of toy cubical blocks. Have students build cubes corresponding to the dimensions in Figure 10–2, that is, one block by itself; a cube consisting of $2 \times 2 \times 2$ blocks; and a cube consisting of $3 \times 3 \times 3$ blocks.

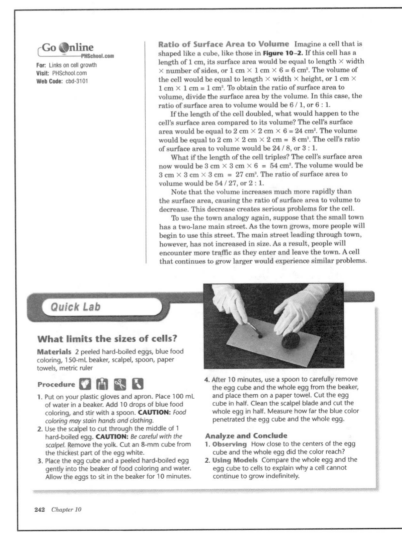

After Reading (continued) Call students' attention to the term *cell division* on the Word Wall. Lead a discussion to clarify that during this process, one cell divides into two new cells, which are called "daughter cells." Ask ELL students to tell the other students the word *daughter* in their native language. To help students understand why each daughter cell has an increased surface/volume ratio, perform the following demonstration. Put two cubic blocks together so that they form a rectangular solid. Have students count the squares that comprise the block's surface area (10). Separate the two cubes and have students count the surface squares on each cube (6 each, 12 total). Make certain that students understand that *replicate* means *copy* by providing an example, such as a page replicated by a copying machine.

Quick Lab—What Limits the Sizes of Cells?

Have students work in pairs; if possible, pair an ELL student with an English-proficient student who also speaks the ELL student's native language. Before allowing students to begin, make sure that the ELL students understand the caution statements (and that all students understand the safety symbols). Allow ELL students to answer the questions with diagrams instead of, or in combination with, words.

Assessing the Lesson

Section Assessment

Modify the material in the Section Assessment to accommodate different language levels. Give English Language Learners who are not proficient enough to write out complete answers the opportunity to demonstrate understanding through diagrams and/or spoken phrases and simple sentences.

To help with question 4, draw a sketch of the imaginary cell and label its dimensions. Also, provide the formulas for surface area and volume. Express the ratio of surface area to volume as a fraction, that is, surface area divided by volume.

Connecting Concepts

List the cell's organelles on the board. Assign one (not two) organelle to each English Language Learner. Then pair students; each student in the pair should have been assigned a different organelle. Have students work together to answer the question.

Ratio of Surface Area to Volume in Cells

Cell Size	1 cm (1 cm × 1 cm)	2 cm (2 cm × 2 cm)	3 cm (3 cm × 3 cm)
Surface Area (length × width × 6)	1 cm × 1 cm × 6 = 6 cm²	2 cm × 2 cm × 6 = 24 cm²	3 cm × 3 cm × 6 = 54 cm²
Volume (length × width × height)	1 cm × 1 cm × 1 cm = 1 cm³	2 cm × 2 cm × 2 cm = 8 cm³	3 cm × 3 cm × 3 cm = 27 cm³
Ratio of Surface Area to Volume	6 / 1 = 6 : 1	24 / 8 = 3 : 1	54 / 27 = 2 : 1

If a cell got too large, it would be more difficult to get sufficient amounts of oxygen and nutrients in and waste products out. This is one reason why cells do not grow much larger even if the organism of which they are a part does.

▲ **Figure 10–2** As the length of a cell increases, its volume increases faster than its surface area. ⊘ The resulting decrease in the cell's ratio of surface area to volume makes it more difficult for the cell to move needed materials in and waste products out.

Division of the Cell

Before it becomes too large, a growing cell divides forming two "daughter" cells. The process by which a cell divides into two new daughter cells is called **cell division.**

Before cell division occurs, the cell replicates, or copies, all of its DNA. This replication of DNA solves the problem of information storage because each daughter cell gets one complete set of genetic information. Thus, each daughter cell receives its own genetic "library." Cell division also solves the problem of increasing size by reducing cell volume. Each daughter cell has an increased ratio of surface area to volume. This allows efficient exchange of materials with the environment.

10–1 Section Assessment

1. ⊘ **Key Concept** Give two reasons why cells divide.

2. How is a cell's DNA like the books in a library?

3. As a cell increases in size, which increases more rapidly, its surface area or its volume?

4. **Critical Thinking Calculating** Calculate the surface area, volume, and ratio of surface area to volume of an imaginary cubic cell measuring 4 cm on each side.

Connecting ⊂ Concepts

Stability and Equilibrium
Select two cell organelles and describe how their functions might be impaired if the cell were to become too large. A review of Chapter 7 may help you with this task.

Cell Growth and Division **243**

Section 10–2
Cell Division

Preparing the Lesson

Assess Prior Knowledge

Read aloud the first paragraph in the section ("What do you think would happen . . ."). To help students understand this paragraph, continue the library analogy introduced in Section 10–1. Ask: Suppose a community decides that it needs to build a new library. Once the new library is built, could you just take half the books from the old library and move them to the new library? For example, could you divide each set of encyclopedias into two sets? Could you divide fiction authors into two groups, and leave books by half the authors in the old library and move the other half to the new library? To help beginning-level ELLs understand this idea, take a set of encyclopedias and separate them into two sets—or take a photo of a set of encyclopedias and tear it down the middle. Help students see that when both cells and libraries divide, they need to receive duplicate sets of certain materials. To demonstrate this visually, you might make copies of a picture of encyclopedias or other books. Make a large "prohibition sign" (slash mark through a circle) over the torn-apart set; write "yes" next to pictures of two separate sets.

Review the concept of genetic information, making sure that students understand that genetic information in cells directs essential cellular activities, and that cells cannot survive without genetic information. Point out the chromosome in Figure 10–3, and tell students that the genetic information in most cells is found in chromosomes.

Vocabulary

Continue the Word Wall that you began in Section 10–1, adding the Vocabulary terms for this section. Write the definitions of each term and show a visual representation of each term. (For pictures of the phases in the cell cycle, you might photocopy Figure 10–5 and cut out the pictures of each individual phase.)

Write the following terms on the board, in this order: *interphase, prophase, metaphase, anaphase,* and *telophase.* For each word, draw a line dividing the prefix from the base word *phase.* Explain that a phase is a stage of some process, and clarify this

---

10–2 Cell Division

Guide for Reading

Key Concepts
- What are the main events of the cell cycle?
- What are the four phases of mitosis?

Vocabulary
mitosis
cytokinesis
chromatid
centromere
interphase
cell cycle
prophase
centriole
spindle
metaphase
anaphase
telophase

**Reading Strategy:
Outlining** As you read this section, outline the major events of the cell cycle. Write a few sentences to describe the activity of chromosomes as they progress through each part of the cell cycle.

What do you think would happen if a cell were simply to split into two, without any advance preparation? Would each daughter cell have everything it needed to survive? Because each cell has only one set of genetic information, the answer is no. Every cell must first copy its genetic information before cell division begins. Each daughter cell then gets a complete copy of that information.

In most prokaryotes, the rest of the process of cell division is a simple matter of separating the contents of the cell into two parts. In eukaryotes, cell division is more complex and occurs in two main stages. The first stage, division of the cell nucleus, is called **mitosis** (my-TOH-sis). The second stage, division of the cytoplasm, is called **cytokinesis** (sy-toh-kih-NEE-sis).

Many organisms, especially unicellular ones, reproduce by means of mitosis and cytokinesis. Reproduction by mitosis is classified as asexual, since the cells produced by mitosis are genetically identical to the parent cell. Mitosis is also the source of new cells when a multicellular organism grows and develops. In humans, for example, mitosis begins shortly after the egg is fertilized, producing the vast numbers of cells needed for the embryo to take form.

Chromosomes

In eukaryotic cells, the genetic information that is passed on from one generation of cells to the next is carried by chromosomes. Chromosomes are made up of DNA—which carries the cell's coded genetic information—and proteins. The cells of every organism have a specific number of chromosomes. The cells of fruit flies, for example, have 8 chromosomes; human cells have 46 chromosomes; and carrot cells have 18 chromosomes.

Chromosomes are not visible in most cells except during cell division. This is because the DNA and protein molecules that make up the chromosomes are spread throughout the nucleus. At the beginning of cell division, however, the chromosomes condense into compact, visible structures that can be seen through a light microscope.

Well before cell division, each chromosome is replicated, or copied. Because of this, each chromosome consists of two identical "sister" **chromatids** (KROH-muh-tidz), as shown in **Figure 10–3.** When the cell divides, the "sister" chromatids separate from each other. One chromatid goes to each of the two new cells.

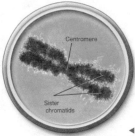

Centromere

Sister chromatids

(magnification: 20,000×)

◀ **Figure 10–3** This is a human chromosome shown as it appears through an electron microscope. Each chromosome has two sister chromatids attached at the centromere. **Inferring** *Why is it important that the sister chromatids are identical?*

244 Chapter 10

---

with specific examples (such as phases of the moon, phases of a journey). Explain that the terms you wrote on the board are the phases, or stages, in the cell cycle.

Reading Strategy

If possible, pair beginning ELL students with advanced ELLs. Have students' outlines focus on the events of mitosis and cytokinesis. They can refer to Figures 10–5 and 10–6 to make their outlines. Accept illustrations rather than (or in addition to) written or oral descriptions.

Reading the Lesson

Chromosomes

You may want to spend minimal time on this part of the text with ELL students. However, make certain that students understand the meanings of chromosomes, DNA, chromatids, and centromeres. Use the Word Wall and Figure 10–3 to clarify these terms.

The Cell Cycle

Before Reading To help students understand what a cycle is, display a picture of a bicycle and ask students what the wheels do (go around and around, over and over). Ask for volunteers to identify other types of cycles, such as the cycle of the seasons and/or the cycles of matter described in Chapter 3. Relate these examples to the cell cycle. Read the boldface sentence aloud. Help students understand that the term "daughter cells" does not indicate that the new cells are female. To help students understand Figure 10–4, note that interphase is divided into three subphases—G_1, S, G_2. Also note that mitosis is divided into five phases, and that students will learn more about these phases later.

During Reading To help students understand the overview of the cell cycle expressed in the boldface sentence, draw a cycle diagram on the board that identifies its three major events (growth, preparing for division, division into two daughter cells; then back to growth). Suggest that students copy the diagram and draw pictures to represent growth and division into two daughter cells.

After Reading Students can work in pairs to list the three phases into which interphase is divided (G_1, S, G_2) as row heads in a table. The column head should be What Happens During the Phase. Students will use this table as they read the text following the next heading, Events of the Cell Cycle. Draw the table on the board, too, in preparation for filling it in.

Each pair of chromatids is attached at an area called the centromere (SEN-troh-meer). **Centromeres** are usually located near the middle of the chromatids, although some lie near the ends. A human body cell entering cell division contains 46 chromosomes, each of which consists of two chromatids.

The Cell Cycle

At one time, biologists described the life of a cell as one cell division after another separated by an "in-between" period of growth called **interphase.** We now appreciate that a great deal happens in the time between cell divisions, and use a concept known as the cell cycle to represent recurring events in the life of the cell. The **cell cycle** is the series of events that cells go through as they grow and divide. **During the cell cycle, a cell grows, prepares for division, and divides to form two daughter cells, each of which then begins the cycle again.** The cell cycle is shown in **Figure 10–4.**

The cell cycle consists of four phases. Mitosis and cytokinesis take place during the M phase. Chromosome replication, or synthesis, takes place during the S phase. When the cell copies the chromosomes, it makes a duplicate set of DNA. Between the M and S phases are G_1 and G_2. The G in the names of these phases stands for "gap," but the G_1 and G_2 are definitely not periods when nothing takes place. They are actually periods of intense growth and activity.

Events of the Cell Cycle

During the normal cell cycle, interphase can be quite long, whereas the process of cell division takes place quickly. Interphase is divided into three phases: G_1, S, and G_2.

The G_1 phase is a period of activity in which cells do most of their growing. During this phase, cells increase in size and synthesize new proteins and organelles.

G_1 is followed by the S phase, in which chromosomes are replicated and the synthesis of DNA molecules takes place. Key proteins associated with the chromosomes are also synthesized during the S phase. Usually, once a cell enters the S phase and begins the replication of its chromosomes, it completes the rest of the cell cycle.

When the DNA replication is completed, the cell enters the G_2 phase. G_2 is usually the shortest of the three phases of interphase. During the G_2 phase, many of the organelles and molecules required for cell division are produced. When the events of the G_2 phase are completed, the cell is ready to enter the M phase and begin the process of cell division.

✔CHECKPOINT *What happens during the G_1 phase?*

Go Online
-NSTA- SCi*LINKS*
For: Links on the cell cycle
Visit: www.SciLinks.org
Web Code: cbn-3103

▼ **Figure 10–4** During the cell cycle, the cell grows, replicates its DNA, and divides into two daughter cells. DNA synthesis takes place during the S phase. Cell division takes place during the M phase. G_1 and G_2 are gap phases.

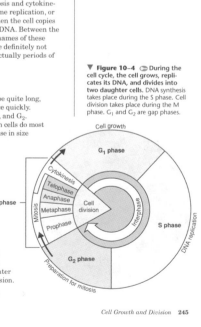

Cell Growth and Division **245**

Events of the Cell Cycle (page 245)

Before Reading Tell students that this part of the lesson focuses on interphase. Refer to the Word Wall for the definition of interphase. Write the word *interphase* on the board, and draw a line separating the prefix *inter-* from the root word *phase.* Explain that the prefix *inter-* often means "between," and that a phase is usually one event in a cycle, as in the phases of the moon. In the cell cycle, interphase is the phase between cell divisions. On the board, write some other words with the prefix *inter-*, such as *interdependence, interlock,* and *international,* and explore the relationship between the prefix and the base words.

Review the letters that designate the stages of interphase (G_1, S, G_2) and what the letters represent: G means "gap," although, as the text says, many important processes continue during the G phases, and S stands for synthesis, specifically DNA synthesis.

Call students' attention to Figure 10–4 on page 245. (If you have the transparency of this illustration—Transparency 141— use an overhead projector to display it.) Help students separate interphase into stages by covering the cell-division wedge with a piece of paper and focusing specifically on the interphase part of the cycle diagram. Point to the central purple circle, and use gestures to show that their reading will now focus on the events of interphase, which are all touched by this circle.

During Reading Pair beginning ELLs with students who speak the same native language but are more proficient in English. Have them work together to complete the tables they constructed when they read "The Cell Cycle" on page 245. They should fill in the events of the three subphases of interphase—G_1, S, G_2.

After Reading Circulate among the groups and check their tables to ensure that they have been completed correctly. Then conduct a class discussion in which you ask volunteers to help you complete the table that you drew on the board. After the table has been completed, refer students again to Figure 10–4. Call on students, including ELLs, to point to each subphase of interphase on the diagram, and to explain, in their own words, what happens during that phase.

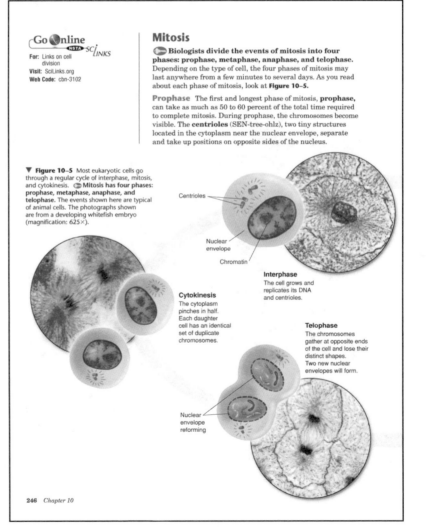

Go Online
NSTA *SciLINKS*
For: Links on cell division
Visit: SciLinks.org
Web Code: cbn-3102

Mitosis

Biologists divide the events of mitosis into four phases: prophase, metaphase, anaphase, and telophase. Depending on the type of cell, the four phases of mitosis may last anywhere from a few minutes to several days. As you read about each phase of mitosis, look at **Figure 10–5.**

Prophase The first and longest phase of mitosis, **prophase,** can take as much as 50 to 60 percent of the total time required to complete mitosis. During prophase, the chromosomes become visible. The **centrioles** (SEN-tree-ohlz), two tiny structures located in the cytoplasm near the nuclear envelope, separate and take up positions on opposite sides of the nucleus.

▼ **Figure 10–5** Most eukaryotic cells go through a regular cycle of interphase, mitosis, and cytokinesis. Mitosis has four phases: prophase, metaphase, anaphase, and telophase. The events shown here are typical of animal cells. The photographs shown are from a developing whitefish embryo (magnification: 625×).

Centrioles

Nuclear envelope

Chromatin

Interphase
The cell grows and replicates its DNA and centrioles.

Cytokinesis
The cytoplasm pinches in half. Each daughter cell has an identical set of duplicate chromosomes.

Telophase
The chromosomes gather at opposite ends of the cell and lose their distinct shapes. Two new nuclear envelopes will form.

Nuclear envelope reforming

246 *Chapter 10*

Mitosis

Before Reading Pronounce the word *mitosis* and use the Word Wall to review the definition of mitosis. Once again, focus students' attention on the cell cycle diagram in Figure 10–4 on page 245. Ask a volunteer to point to the part of the diagram during which mitosis takes place. For the benefit of ELL students, hold the book up and point to this part yourself. Trace the mitosis section in the diagram with your finger and have the ELL students trace it along with you. To help clarify that the phases of mitosis are indicated in orange on the diagram, you might write the word *mitosis* on an orange card and point to the orange wedges in the diagram.

Use the Word Wall to review the other terms in this part of the text. In particular, many students confuse the terms *centrioles, centromeres,* and *centrosomes,* because all three words begin with the prefix *centr-,* meaning "center." (You may want to avoid the term *centrosome* entirely with your ELLs, because it is possible to understand the process of mitosis without knowing the meaning of that term.) Use Figure 10–3 on page 244 to help students see that a centromere is a structure located roughly at the center of a chromosome. In Figure 10–5, the interphase and prophase stages in the diagram can be used to show what centrioles are and how they relate to the mitotic spindle.

After reviewing the science terms, instruct students to look more closely at Figure 10–5. (If you have Transparency 142, display it using an overhead projector.) Have students relate the phases shown in Figure 10–5 to the phases in the cycle diagram in Figure 10–4. Make sure that students understand that the diagrams show what is happening in the photos. Also ascertain that all students know the order in which the phases occur, and that they are shown in clockwise order to correspond to the cycle. To clarify this, you might distribute copies of Figure 10-5 with Prophase numbered 1, Metaphase numbered 2, and so forth. If you do distribute copies, have students draw arrows from one phase to the next.

Read aloud the captions in Figure 10–5, pointing to the relevant parts of each diagram and photo. Point out that with the exception of the diagram/photo for Interphase, each of the parts of the figure has a corresponding subhead in the text that students will read.

During Reading Call on a volunteer to read the boldface sentence (page 246) aloud. Point out that the green headings discuss each one of the phases in the order in which they appear in the boldface sentence. Encourage students to refer to Figure 10–5 as they read. If they have copies, encourage students to make notes on their copies.

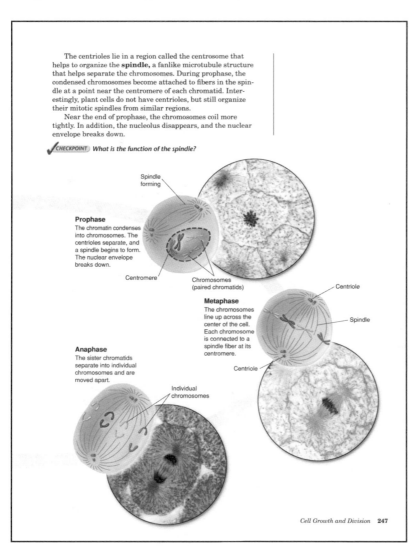

The centrioles lie in a region called the centrosome that helps to organize the **spindle,** a fanlike microtubule structure that helps separate the chromosomes. During prophase, the condensed chromosomes become attached to fibers in the spindle at a point near the centromere of each chromatid. Interestingly, plant cells do not have centrioles, but still organize their mitotic spindles from similar regions.

Near the end of prophase, the chromosomes coil more tightly. In addition, the nucleolus disappears, and the nuclear envelope breaks down.

CHECKPOINT *What is the function of the spindle?*

Spindle forming

Prophase
The chromatin condenses into chromosomes. The centrioles separate, and a spindle begins to form. The nuclear envelope breaks down.

Centromere

Chromosomes (paired chromatids)

Centriole

Metaphase
The chromosomes line up across the center of the cell. Each chromosome is connected to a spindle fiber at its centromere.

Spindle

Anaphase
The sister chromatids separate into individual chromosomes and are moved apart.

Centriole

Individual chromosomes

Cell Growth and Division **247**

After Reading Pair beginning ELLs with ELLs who speak the same native language but are more proficient in English. Students can collaborate on constructing tables that describe each stage of mitosis. The row headings should name the stages, beginning with Prophase. Label the column heads Picture and What Happens. In the Picture column, students should draw a sketch showing what happens in each stage of mitosis. In the What Happens column, they should write sentences, phrases, or words—depending on their level of English proficiency—describing what happens in each stage. (Beginning ELLs will not be capable of writing sentences, but they can use phrases; their partners should help them choose words.) Each student should make his or her own chart, but the members of each pair should collaborate in their ideas and should review each other's work. Students should save their completed charts to study and use for review.

Cytokinesis

Before Reading Have students use the charts that they completed on the phases of mitosis to review the events of telophase. Ask students to describe or illustrate the state of chromosomes and nuclei in the two daughter cells during telophase. Review the meanings of *nuclear envelope* and *cytoplasm* by pointing to the appropriate parts of the cell in Figure 10–5 on page 246. Then read aloud the first paragraph under the heading Cytokinesis. Use the Word Wall to review the definition of *cytokinesis*.

Focus students' attention on Figure 10–6. Point out that the photograph and the diagram show cytokinesis in plant cells. Point to the nuclei and cytoplasm in the photo and diagram. Then point to the cell plate. Ask: How many cells are there now? When a volunteer answers, write the numeral 2 on the board and point to the two new cells.

During Reading Now have students with some English proficiency silently read the second paragraph under the heading, telling them to refer to Figure 10–6 as they read. Take beginning level ELLs aside and read the paragraph aloud. As you read about cytokinesis in plant cells, point to what is happening in Figure 10–6.

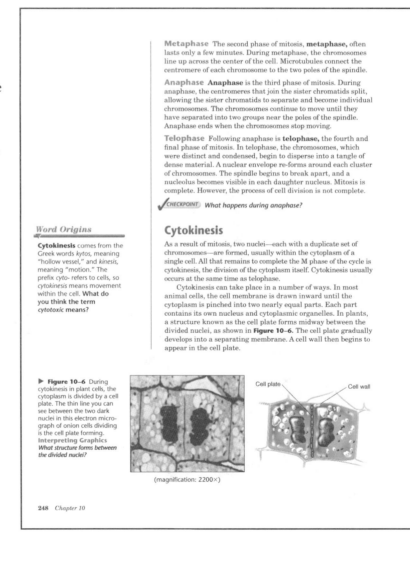

Metaphase The second phase of mitosis, **metaphase,** often lasts only a few minutes. During metaphase, the chromosomes line up across the center of the cell. Microtubules connect the centromere of each chromosome to the two poles of the spindle.

Anaphase **Anaphase** is the third phase of mitosis. During anaphase, the centromeres that join the sister chromatids split, allowing the sister chromatids to separate and become individual chromosomes. The chromosomes continue to move until they have separated into two groups near the poles of the spindle. Anaphase ends when the chromosomes stop moving.

Telophase Following anaphase is **telophase,** the fourth and final phase of mitosis. In telophase, the chromosomes, which were distinct and condensed, begin to disperse into a tangle of dense material. A nuclear envelope re-forms around each cluster of chromosomes. The spindle begins to break apart, and a nucleolus becomes visible in each daughter nucleus. Mitosis is complete. However, the process of cell division is not complete.

✓ **CHECKPOINT** *What happens during anaphase?*

Word Origins

Cytokinesis comes from the Greek words *kytos,* meaning "hollow vessel," and *kinesis,* meaning "motion." The prefix *cyto-* refers to cells, so *cytokinesis* means movement within the cell. **What do you think the term *cytotoxic* means?**

Cytokinesis

As a result of mitosis, two nuclei—each with a duplicate set of chromosomes—are formed, usually within the cytoplasm of a single cell. All that remains to complete the M phase of the cycle is cytokinesis, the division of the cytoplasm itself. Cytokinesis usually occurs at the same time as telophase.

Cytokinesis can take place in a number of ways. In most animal cells, the cell membrane is drawn inward until the cytoplasm is pinched into two nearly equal parts. Each part contains its own nucleus and cytoplasmic organelles. In plants, a structure known as the cell plate forms midway between the divided nuclei, as shown in **Figure 10–6.** The cell plate gradually develops into a separating membrane. A cell wall then begins to appear in the cell plate.

▶ **Figure 10–6** During cytokinesis in plant cells, the cytoplasm is divided by a cell plate. The thin line you can see between the two dark nuclei in this electron micrograph of onion cells dividing is the cell plate forming. **Interpreting Graphics** *What structure forms between the divided nuclei?*

Cell plate   Cell wall

(magnification: 2200×)

248   *Chapter 10*

After Reading Have students work in small groups to diagram how cytokinesis occurs in plant and animal cells. They should label their drawings Cytokinesis in Plant Cells and Cytokinesis in Animal Cells. For plant cells, students can copy Figure 10–6 on page 248; for animal cells, students should refer to the second and third sentences in the second paragraph following the heading. Circulate among groups, checking that illustrations demonstrate comprehension, particularly for the process in animal cells, since it is not illustrated. Also check to make sure students can differentiate between the processes in plant and animal cells by covering the titles of their illustrations and asking whether each shows plant or animal cytokinesis. Finally, students in the groups should work together to write words, phrases, or sentences that describe the process of cytokinesis in plant and animal cells.

At this point, you may want students to perform the Exploration on pages 254–255, Modeling the Phases of the Cell Cycle. This activity will visually reinforce and supplement their understanding of the events in the cell cycle.

Analyzing Data—Life Spans of Human Cells

Preteach or review any terms that might be difficult, e.g., *life span, formulating hypotheses.* Help students understand the meaning of the three column heads in the table, and the information in the rows. For example, to illustrate "can divide," you might draw one cell with an arrow that leads to two new cells; for "cannot divide," use a similar drawing but draw a slash mark or an x through the arrow and two new cells.

Have students work in pairs or groups of three. Encourage ELL students to create their own illustrations as substitutes or supplements for written answers to the questions.

Assessing the Lesson

Section Assessment

Modify the questions to accommodate ELLs' lack of English proficiency. For students at the lower level of English proficiency, choose questions that can be answered with illustrations accompanied by words or simple phrases and sentences. Encourage students to use as much English as they know. Accept their responses either orally or in written form.

Analyzing Data

Life Spans of Human Cells

Like all organisms, cells have a given life span from birth to death. In multicellular organisms, such as humans, the health of the organism depends on cells not exceeding their life span. This is especially true of cells that tend to divide rapidly. If these cells did not die on schedule, overcrowding of cells would occur, causing uncontrolled growth that would be life-threatening.

The data table shows the life spans of various human cells. It also contains information about the ability of the cells to multiply through cell division.

1. **Inferring** White blood cells help protect the body from infection and disease-producing organisms. How might their function relate to their life span?

2. **Comparing and Contrasting** Based on the data, how are the consequences of injuries to the heart and spinal cord similar to each other? How are they different from the consequences of injuries to smooth muscle?

3. **Formulating Hypotheses** Propose a hypothesis to account for the data related to the cell life spans of the lining of the esophagus, small intestine, and large intestine.

Life Spans of Various Human Cells		
Cell Type	Life Span	Cell Division
Lining of esophagus	2–3 days	Can divide
Lining of small intestine	1–2 days	Can divide
Lining of large intestine	6 days	Can divide
Red blood cells	Less than 120 days	Cannot divide
White blood cells	10 hours to decades	Cannot divide
Smooth muscle	Long-lived	Can divide
Cardiac (heart) muscle	Long-lived	Cannot divide
Skeletal muscle	Long-lived	Cannot divide
Neuron (nerve cell)	Long-lived	Most do not divide

4. **Going Further** Cancer is a disease related to cell life span and cell division. If cancer cells were added to the data table, predict what would be written under the columns headed "Life Span" and "Cell Division." Explain the reasoning underlying your predictions.

10–2 Section Assessment

1. ○ **Key Concept** Name the main events of the cell cycle.
2. ○ **Key Concept** Describe what happens during each of the four phases of mitosis.
3. Describe what happens during interphase.
4. What are chromosomes made of?
5. How do prokaryotic cells divide?
6. **Critical Thinking Comparing and Contrasting** How is cytokinesis in plant cells similar to cytokinesis in animal cells? How is it different?

Writing in Science

Creative Writing
Suppose you were small enough to hitch a ride on a chromosome located in a plant cell that goes through mitosis and cytokinesis. Describe what you would see happening during each phase of the process.

Cell Growth and Division **249**

Section 10–3
Regulating the Cell Cycle

Preparing the Lesson

Assess Prior Knowledge

Write the following on the board:

regulating = controlling

regulate = control

Explain that the heading Regulating the Cell Cycle means the same thing as "controlling the cell cycle." Ask volunteers to explain what it means to control something. If possible, have ELLs who are more proficient in English explain the concept of regulation/control to beginners in their native language. Display different pictures that help clarify the process of controlling something—for example, a crossing guard or stoplight controlling motor and pedestrian traffic; a hand operating a faucet or hose nozzle to control the flow of water; a hand using a remote-control device to adjust the volume on a television. Ask what might happen if each of these processes could not be regulated. Use these examples as a way of leading to the regulation of the cell cycle and why it is necessary.

Vocabulary

Add the words *cyclin* and *cancer*, along with their definitions, to the Word Wall that you began earlier. Also add other words with which ELL students might need help, such as *protein, eukaryotic, petri dish*, and *experiment*.

After you introduce the word *cancer* and its definition, ask for volunteers to say the word or phrase for cancer in their native languages, and to explain its entire meaning. (Some languages may not have an exact equivalent of the English word *cancer,* or the equivalent word or phrase may mean something slightly different than the concept does in English.)

Reading Strategy

Have students work in small groups to complete their summaries. The summaries of ELL students can take several forms: a written summary in their native language if you speak that language; illustrations that show the processes; or illustrations accompanied by simple English phrases or sentences.

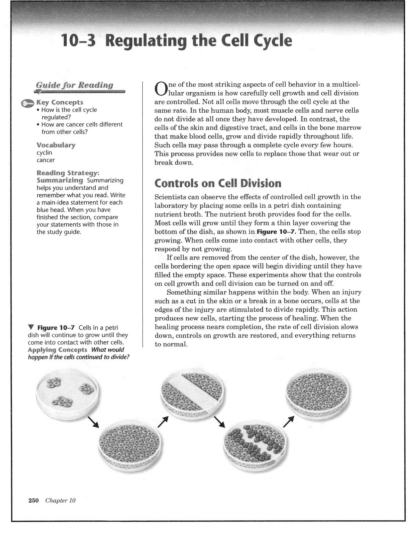

10–3 Regulating the Cell Cycle

Guide for Reading

Key Concepts
- How is the cell cycle regulated?
- How are cancer cells different from other cells?

Vocabulary
cyclin
cancer

Reading Strategy:
Summarizing Summarizing helps you understand and remember what you read. Write a main-idea statement for each blue head. When you have finished the section, compare your statements with those in the study guide.

One of the most striking aspects of cell behavior in a multicellular organism is how carefully cell growth and cell division are controlled. Not all cells move through the cell cycle at the same rate. In the human body, most muscle cells and nerve cells do not divide at all once they have developed. In contrast, the cells of the skin and digestive tract, and cells in the bone marrow that make blood cells, grow and divide rapidly throughout life. Such cells may pass through a complete cycle every few hours. This process provides new cells to replace those that wear out or break down.

Controls on Cell Division

Scientists can observe the effects of controlled cell growth in the laboratory by placing some cells in a petri dish containing nutrient broth. The nutrient broth provides food for the cells. Most cells will grow until they form a thin layer covering the bottom of the dish, as shown in **Figure 10–7.** Then, the cells stop growing. When cells come into contact with other cells, they respond by not growing.

If cells are removed from the center of the dish, however, the cells bordering the open space will begin dividing until they have filled the empty space. These experiments show that the controls on cell growth and cell division can be turned on and off.

Something similar happens within the body. When an injury such as a cut in the skin or a break in a bone occurs, cells at the edges of the injury are stimulated to divide rapidly. This action produces new cells, starting the process of healing. When the healing process nears completion, the rate of cell division slows down, controls on growth are restored, and everything returns to normal.

▼ **Figure 10–7** Cells in a petri dish will continue to grow until they come into contact with other cells. **Applying Concepts** *What would happen if the cells continued to divide?*

250   *Chapter 10*

Reading the Lesson

Introduction

Before Reading Write the second sentence in the introductory paragraph on page 250 on the board: "Not all cells move through the cell cycle at the same rate." Read the sentence aloud, pointing to each word as you say it. Call on a volunteer to explain what this sentence means. To clarify the concept of differing rates, you might show pictures of runners (or cars) in a race, pointing out that the winner has moved at a faster rate than the others.

During Reading To focus students' reading, tell them to look for information about the cell cycles of the following types of cells: muscle, nerve, skin, digestive tract. Students may take notes during reading. Alternatively, prepare a chart that has subheadings for the different types of cells. Have students supply the information as they read.

After Reading Have volunteers describe the cell cycles of each of the types of cells mentioned.

Controls on Cell Division

Before Reading Call students' attention to Figure 10–7. Read the caption aloud. Call on volunteers, including ELLs, to explain what they think is happening in each part of the illustration. (Explain that in the third petri dish, scientists removed the cells from the center, which is why the empty strip is there.) Ask students to try to explain the significance of the events shown in the illustration. Then read the caption question aloud and ask volunteers to answer it.

During Reading Distribute copies of Figure 10–7. As students read about the experiment, have them label each step with a brief description of what it shows.

After Reading Call on volunteers, including ELLs, to read their labels aloud. Then ask students to explain in words—or illustrate—what happens as a cut in the skin begins to heal.

Cell Cycle Regulators

Before Reading Review the definitions of *cyclin, eukaryotic cell, cytoplasm,* and *mitotic spindle.* Write the following boldface sentence on the board: "Cyclins regulate the timing of the cell cycle in eukaryotic cells." Say it out loud and point to each word as you say it. Then have the students read the sentence aloud together. Ask: What do you think you will be reading about?

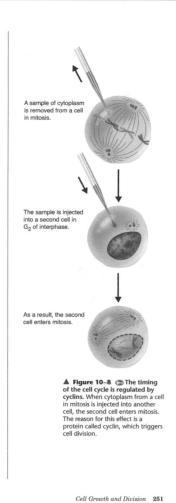

Cell Cycle Regulators

For many years, biologists searched for a substance that might regulate the cell cycle—something that would "tell" cells when it was time to divide, duplicate their chromosomes, or enter another phase of the cycle. In the early 1980s, biologists found the substance.

Several scientists, including Tim Hunt of Great Britain and Mark Kirschner of the United States, discovered that cells in mitosis contained a protein that when injected into a nondividing cell, would cause a mitotic spindle to form. Such an experiment is shown in **Figure 10–8.** To their surprise, they discovered that the amount of this protein in the cell rose and fell in time with the cell cycle. They decided to call this protein **cyclin** because it seemed to regulate the cell cycle. Investigators have since discovered a family of closely related proteins, known as cyclins, that are involved in cell cycle regulation. ⊙ **Cyclins regulate the timing of the cell cycle in eukaryotic cells.**

The discovery of cyclins was just the beginning. More recently, dozens of other proteins have been discovered that also help to regulate the cell cycle. There are two types of regulatory proteins: those that occur inside the cell and those that occur outside the cell.

Internal Regulators Proteins that respond to events inside the cell are called internal regulators. Internal regulators allow the cell cycle to proceed only when certain processes have happened inside the cell. For example, several regulatory proteins make sure that a cell does not enter mitosis until all its chromosomes have been replicated. Another regulatory protein prevents a cell from entering anaphase until all its chromosomes are attached to the mitotic spindle.

External Regulators Proteins that respond to events outside the cell are called external regulators. External regulators direct cells to speed up or slow down the cell cycle. Growth factors are among the most important external regulators. They stimulate the growth and division of cells. Growth regulators are especially important during embryonic development and wound healing. Molecules found on the surfaces of neighboring cells often have an opposite effect, causing cells to slow down or stop their cell cycles. These signals prevent excessive cell growth and keep the tissues of the body from disrupting each other.

✔CHECKPOINT What are cyclins?

A sample of cytoplasm is removed from a cell in mitosis.

The sample is injected into a second cell in G_2 of interphase.

As a result, the second cell enters mitosis.

▲ **Figure 10–8** ⊙ The timing of the cell cycle is regulated by cyclins. When cytoplasm from a cell in mitosis is injected into another cell, the second cell enters mitosis. The reason for this effect is a protein called cyclin, which triggers cell division.

Cell Growth and Division **251**

Discuss Figure 10–8 (page 251) with students. Read the major caption and the smaller captions aloud. Ask what the phrase "as a result" means in the third of the smaller captions. Help students understand the cause-effect relationship by drawing a blank cause-effect chart on the board. (Cause-effect charts are discussed on page 31 of this Handbook.) Fill in the Cause row and read what you have written aloud. Then ask an ELL student to tell you the effect, or to point to it in Figure 10–8. Write the effect in the chart. Then review the phrase "as a result," explaining that this phrase usually indicates the effect in a cause-effect relationship.

Review the concept of regulation/control. Focus students' attention on the green headings Internal Regulators and External Regulators. Write the words *internal* and *external* on the board, drawing lines separating the prefixes *in-* and *ex-* from the base word. Explain what these prefixes mean. You might use a semi-closed container to demonstrate the difference between *internal* and *external.* Put your hand in the container to indicate *internal;* lay your hand on the outside of the container to indicate *external.* Ask for other words that begin with these prefixes (e.g., *inside, interior, exit, exterior*). Then tell students that internal regulators respond to events inside the cell, while external regulators respond to events outside the cell. As you do this, point to the inside and outside of a diagram of a cell.

During Reading You might have the ELL students skip most of the first two paragraphs and begin their reading with the boldface sentence. As students read about internal and external regulators, have them take notes in a T-chart, which is a chart with two headings at the top, and a line that separates the two. The headings for their T chart should be Internal Regulators and External Regulators.

After Reading Have students review their charts in groups composed of both ELL and English-proficient students. Circulate among the groups, helping the ELL students and correcting any misconceptions.

Uncontrolled Cell Growth

Before Reading Use the Word Wall to review the term *cancer.* Work with the class to create a concept circle indicating what students already know—or think they know—about cancer. (Concept circles are discussed on page 29 of this Handbook.) Make sure to elicit contributions from ELL students. In your post-reading discussion, correct any misconceptions.

(magnification: 6900×)

▲ **Figure 10–9** Cancer cells do not respond to the signals that regulate the growth of most cells. Masses of cancer cells form tumors that can damage normal tissues. These cancer cells are from a cancer tumor in the large intestine.

To find out more about how scientists study cancer, view the segment "Skin Cancer: Deadly Cells," on Videotape Two.

Uncontrolled Cell Growth

Why is cell growth regulated so carefully? The principal reason may be that the consequences of uncontrolled cell growth in a multicellular organism are very severe. **Cancer,** a disorder in which some of the body's own cells lose the ability to control growth, is one such example. ⊕ **Cancer cells do not respond to the signals that regulate the growth of most cells.** As a result, they divide uncontrollably and form masses of cells called tumors that can damage the surrounding tissues. Cancer cells may break loose from tumors and spread throughout the body, disrupting normal activities and causing serious medical problems or even death. **Figure 10–9** shows typical cancer cells.

What causes the loss of growth control that characterizes cancer? The various forms of cancer have many causes, including smoking tobacco, radiation exposure, and even viral infection. All cancers, however, have one thing in common: The control over the cell cycle has broken down. Some cancer cells will no longer respond to external growth regulators, while others fail to produce the internal regulators that ensure orderly growth.

An astonishing number of cancer cells have a defect in a gene called p53, which normally halts the cell cycle until all chromosomes have been properly replicated. Damaged or defective p53 genes cause the cells to lose the information needed to respond to signals that would normally control their growth.

Cancer is a serious disease. Understanding and combating cancer remains a major scientific challenge, but scientists at least know where to start. Cancer is a disease of the cell cycle, and conquering cancer will require a much deeper understanding of the processes that control cell division.

10–3 Section Assessment

1. ⊕ **Key Concept** What chemicals regulate the cell cycle? How do they work?
2. ⊕ **Key Concept** What happens when cells do not respond to the signals that normally regulate their growth?
3. How do cells respond to contact with other cells?
4. Why can cancer be considered a disease of the cell cycle?
5. **Critical Thinking Formulating Hypotheses** Write a hypothesis about what you think would happen if cyclin were injected into a cell that was in mitosis.

Alternative Assessment

Designing an Anticancer Drug
Imagine that you are developing a drug that will inhibit the growth of cancer cells. Use your knowledge of the cell cycle to describe how the drug would target and prevent the multiplication of cancer cells. Use the Internet to compare your anticancer drug with those currently in use.

252   *Chapter 10*

Before Reading (continued) Call attention to Figure 10–9, and explain that it shows cancer cells. Read the caption aloud, including the boldface sentence. Ask students what is meant by the phrase "signals that regulate the growth of most cells." Help students recall that proteins, including cyclins, regulate the cell cycle.

During Reading To focus students' reading, have students look for answers to the following questions and take notes as they read:

1. Why is cell growth regulated carefully?
2. What is cancer?
3. In what way are cancer cells different from normal cells?
4. What is the function of the gene called p53?
5. What has happened to this gene in most cancer cells?

After Reading Call on volunteers to share their answers as a whole class or to do collaborative sharing. (Members of a group, each consisting of three or four students, compare answers as you circulate among the groups.)

Assessing the Lesson

Section Assessment

Assess ELL students with other students but modify the questions to the concept or vocabulary that is aligned with the English-language proficiency level of each student. For example, students who are at the lower level of English proficiency may need to use illustrations, phrases, or simple sentences.

Alternative Assessment

ELL students can create diagrams that show how their drug would interfere with the cell cycle.

Stem Cells: Promises and Problems

Before Reading Use the diagram and photos on this page to define *stem cells* and add the term to the Word Wall. You may also need to preteach other terms, such as *neurons, paralysis, heart valves, diabetes, embryos, moral,* and *ethical.*

During Reading Use the headings as a way of focusing reading by rephrasing them as questions: What medical problems might stem cells help? Where do scientists get stem cells?

After Reading Group students for a discussion, making sure that all language levels are represented in each group. Circulate to make certain that ELL students understand the issue; respect all students' opinions. ELLs should be paired with English-proficient students to do research.

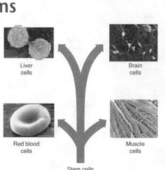

TECHNOLOGY & SOCIETY

Stem Cells: Promises and Problems

Where do the different cells and tissues in your body come from? Incredible as it seems, every cell was produced by mitosis from a small number of cells called stem cells. Stem cells are unspecialized cells that have the potential to differentiate—to become specialized in structure and function—into a wide variety of cell types. In early embryonic development, stem cells produce every tissue in the body. Evidence indicates that stem cells also are found in adults. Stem cells in the bone marrow, for example, produce more than a dozen types of blood cells, replacing those lost due to normal wear and tear.

Stem Cells in Medicine

Although your body produces billions of new cells every day, it is not always able to produce the right kind of cell to replace those damaged by injury or disease. For example, the body is not able to produce new neurons to repair serious spinal cord injuries, such as those that cause paralysis. Because of this, at present, there is no way for doctors to restore movement and feeling to people who are paralyzed.

Stem cells may be the perfect solution to this problem. Recently, researchers have found that implants of stem cells can reverse the effects of brain injuries in mice. There is hope that the same will hold true for humans and that stem cells might be used to reverse brain and spinal cord injuries. It also may be possible to use stem cells to grow new liver tissue, to replace heart valves, and to reverse the effects of diabetes.

Sources of Stem Cells

In 1998, researchers isolated human embryonic stem cells and reported that the cells were capable of growing into various types of tissues. However, obtaining and using cells taken from human embryos raises serious moral and ethical issues. As a result, such research is highly controversial.

The fact that embryonic tissue is genetically different from that of a person who might need a stem-cell transplant presents a problem, too. The immune system of a transplant recipient might reject the stem cells, causing the transplant to fail.

Researchers have found that nerve, muscle, and liver cells sometimes can be grown from adult, human blood-forming stem cells. Experiments such as these, although still in the early stages of development, may usher in an era in which replacement tissue is grown from a person's own stem cells.

Research and Decide

Use library or Internet resources to learn more about stem-cell research. Then, write a brief report on how this technology will impact the future of medicine.

Go Online
PHSchool.com
For: Links from the authors
Visit: PHSchool.com
Web Code: cbe-3104

Cell Growth and Division **253**

Exploration

Modeling the Phases of the Cell Cycle

Explain the expectations of the lab before students begin the lab procedure. Make sure students know that the lab has several aspects: first, students will use a microscope to find onion root cells in various phases of the cell cycle, sketch these cells, and use the sketches as the basis for making models of the phases of the cell cycle; second, students will randomly choose 25 onion root cells, decide which phase of the cell cycle each is in, and record this information in a copy of the data table; and finally, students will arrange their models of the phases of the cell cycle in correct order.

Problem

Review the phases of the cell cycle by referring students to Figures 10–5 and 10–6.

Procedure

If you have not already done so for the Inquiry Activity at the beginning of the chapter, work with ELL students to show them how to use a microscope. Then pair each English language learner with a partner who is at a higher language level and is willing to help the ELL student understand the procedure.

Demonstrate how to locate the onion root tip on the slide, and how to focus the microscope on the appropriate part of the root tip (Steps 1, 2, and 3). Once you or the student's partner have helped ELL students locate appropriate cells to sketch, the ELL students can draw their sketches independently.

Partners should collaborate in selecting materials for the models and constructing the models. Circulate among the pairs, encouraging ELL students to use words to describe their models and to indicate what the different parts of their models represent. For beginners, provide labels that they can use instead of spoken words, such as *chromosome, spindle, prophase,* and so forth.

Partners can collaborate in Step 6, in which they choose 25 root tip cells and decide which phase of the cell cycle each cell is in. Partners should also work together to arrange their models in order.

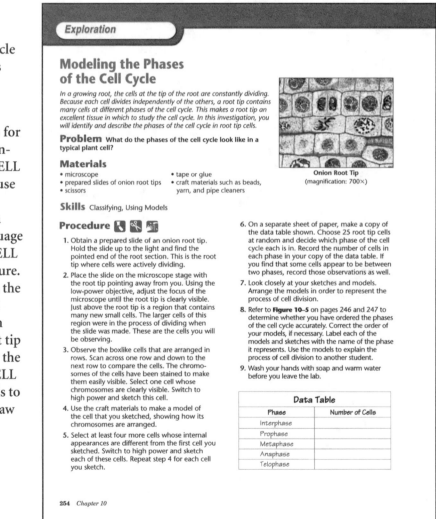

Analyze and Conclude

Many ELL students will have difficulty writing answers to these questions. Allow students' answers to be in the form of simple sentences, phrases, or illustrations. Encourage students to use as much English vocabulary as they know. Allow for less precise wording. For the beginners, where possible, have someone translate the questions.

1. Make certain that ELL students understand that they should use the information in the data table to answer this question.
2. To help students understand the question, you might paraphrase it, for example: What did you see that shows that the phases of mitosis aren't really separate, but blend into one another? ELL students will probably need the help of a partner to answer this question.
3. Have ELL students work with their partners to answer this question.
4. Once ELL students understand the task they must do, they can work either alone or with a partner to think of alternative models. Encourage students to use words to describe their models.
5. To help ELL students, eliminate all but the last two questions from this step ("What process ensures . . . ? During which part . . . ?")

Go Further

To help students understand the multinucleate nature of muscle cells, show them photomicrographs or diagrams from a college anatomy textbook.

Analyze and Conclude

1. **Analyzing Data** Do your results indicate that there were more cells in some phases than in others? Identify the most common phase(s) and explain what these differences in numbers of cells might mean.
2. **Drawing Conclusions** What evidence did you observe that shows mitosis is a continuous process, not a series of separate events?
3. **Using Models** Describe what is happening in each phase of your cell models.
4. **Using Models** Propose an alternative model to illustrate the same concept.
5. **Applying Concepts** Cells in the root divide many times as the root grows longer and thicker. With each cell division, the chromosomes are divided between two daughter cells, yet the number of chromosomes in each cell does not change. What process ensures that the normal number of chromosomes is restored after each cell division? During which part of the cell cycle does this process occur?

Go Further

Making Models In muscle cells, mitosis is not always followed by cell division. Instead, repeated cycles of mitosis result in long, tubular cells with many nuclei. Make a model that shows mitosis in a muscle cell.

Go Online
PHSchool.com

For: Data sharing
Visit: PHSchool.com
Web Code: cbd-3104

Share Your Data Online Enter your data on the number of cells in the phases of the cell cycle. Then, look at the data entered by other students. Based on the available data, were there more cells in some phases than in others? Why might your results differ from those of other students?

Cell Growth and Division **255**

Study Guide

Key Concepts

These are the overarching ideas in each section, and they repeat the boldface sentences. If it is necessary to select only essential content for ELLs, choose these concepts. For beginning-level ELL students, select only essential conceptual words or translate the concepts into the students' native languages.

Vocabulary

All of the listed words should appear on the Word Wall and in the ELL students' glossaries. Suggest that students use their glossaries for review purposes.

Thinking Visually

In this and other chapters, Thinking Visually uses a graphic organizer to give students an opportunity to express important ideas with a minimum of words, and to show the relationships among those ideas. You may need to modify the graphic organizer to help English language learners.

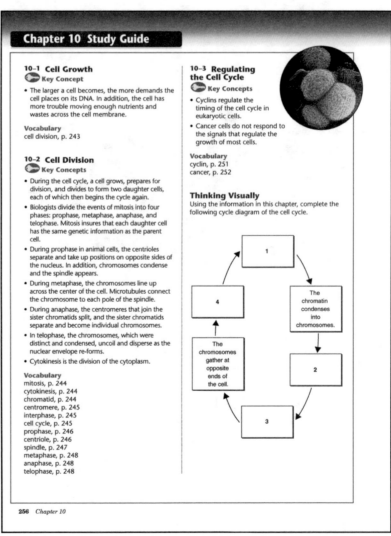

Chapter 10 Study Guide

10–1 Cell Growth

Key Concept

- The larger a cell becomes, the more demands the cell places on its DNA. In addition, the cell has more trouble moving enough nutrients and wastes across the cell membrane.

Vocabulary
cell division, p. 243

10–2 Cell Division

Key Concepts

- During the cell cycle, a cell grows, prepares for division, and divides to form two daughter cells, each of which then begins the cycle again.
- Biologists divide the events of mitosis into four phases: prophase, metaphase, anaphase, and telophase. Mitosis insures that each daughter cell has the same genetic information as the parent cell.
- During prophase in animal cells, the centrioles separate and take up positions on opposite sides of the nucleus. In addition, chromosomes condense and the spindle appears.
- During metaphase, the chromosomes line up across the center of the cell. Microtubules connect the chromosome to each pole of the spindle.
- During anaphase, the centromeres that join the sister chromatids split, and the sister chromatids separate and become individual chromosomes.
- In telophase, the chromosomes, which were distinct and condensed, uncoil and disperse as the nuclear envelope re-forms.
- Cytokinesis is the division of the cytoplasm.

Vocabulary
mitosis, p. 244
cytokinesis, p. 244
chromatid, p. 244
centromere, p. 245
interphase, p. 245
cell cycle, p. 245
prophase, p. 246
centriole, p. 246
spindle, p. 247
metaphase, p. 248
anaphase, p. 248
telophase, p. 248

10–3 Regulating the Cell Cycle

Key Concepts

- Cyclins regulate the timing of the cell cycle in eukaryotic cells.
- Cancer cells do not respond to the signals that regulate the growth of most cells.

Vocabulary
cyclin, p. 251
cancer, p. 252

Thinking Visually
Using the information in this chapter, complete the following cycle diagram of the cell cycle.

1

The chromatin condenses into chromosomes.

2

3

The chromosomes gather at opposite ends of the cell.

4

256   Chapter 10

Transparencies
for
Graphic
Organizers